ANIMALS OF THE WORLD

ANIMALS OF THE WORLD

Dr JIŘÍ FELIX

ILLUSTRATED BY JAROMÍR KNOTEK,
LIBUŠE KNOTKOVÁ, KVĚTOSLAV HÍSEK
AND ALENA ČEPICKÁ

Exeter Books

NEW YORK

First published in the USA 1985
Published by Exeter Books,
Distributed by Bookthrift
Exeter is a trademark of Simon and Schuster, Inc.
Bookthrift is a registered trademark of Simon and Schuster, Inc.
NEW YORK, New York

© Artia, Prague 1984
© Copyright This edition The Hamlyn Publishing Group Limited 1984

Translated by Stephen Finn
Graphic design by Vladimír Šmerda
Photographs by: S. Chvapil, J. Felix, B. Forman, M. Holeček,
J. Jeník, O. Mazůrek, I. Petřík, V. Plešinger, J. Sekyra, V. Šibrava,
I. Šlár, J. Tomas and B. Záruba

ISBN 0-671-07570-5

Printed in Czechoslovakia by TSNP Martin
1/19/03/51-02

CONTENTS

AFRICA

THE AMERICAS

ASIA

EUROPE

AUSTRALASIA

THE OCEANS, SEAS AND POLES

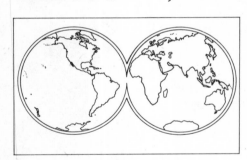

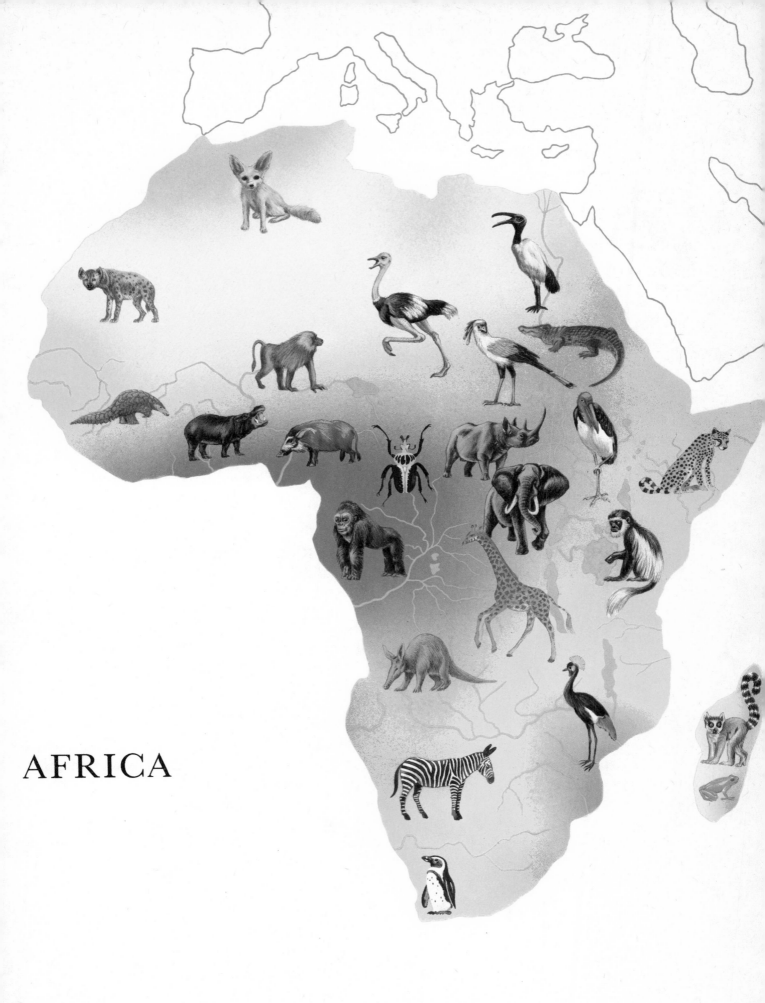

AFRICA

Africa, second largest of the continents, is sometimes also called the Dark Continent. This is because it was not explored by Europeans for so long. The climate is tropical—that is, very hot in most places. Only the countries in the very north and south of Africa are a little cooler: they have a subtropical climate.

Almost a third of the continent is covered by savannahs and grassy plains. Nowhere else in the world can you find such large and varied herds of hoofed mammals as in the African savannahs. Among the most striking of these are giraffes, zebras, and many species of antelopes, which live on grass and the leaves of bushes and trees. During the dry season, when the fierce tropical sun bakes the earth hard, herds of hundreds of thousands of these animals migrate to the areas the drought has not yet reached. Then, as the rainy season brings out shoots of fresh grass and the trees and shrubs turn green again, the animals return to their former homes.

The balance of Nature in the savannahs is maintained by the large beasts of prey, or carnivores. These follow the grazing herds, which provide a constant source of food for them, and this prevents overpopulation among the hoofed mammals.

Large parts of Africa are covered by inhospitable sandy, clayey or stony deserts and semideserts. The biggest of these are the famous Sahara Desert in the north and the Kalahari Desert in the south-west.

A smaller area, about eight per cent of the continent, consists of tropical rainforests. These are mostly in the western part of Africa, though they also occur in the east. One of the best known is the Ituri Jungle in West Africa, home of the Mbuti tribe of pygmies. They still use only primitive weapons to hunt their food—spears, bows and arrows or nets.

Forests can also be found in the savannahs, where they line the banks of the larger rivers; such forests are known as gallery forests.

The longest river in Africa is the Nile, although the River Zaire carries the greatest volume of water. In East Africa there are several large lakes, the biggest of which is Lake Victoria. The swampy regions around the rivers and great lakes provide homes for large numbers of birds, mammals and amphibians. Many species of fish, both large and small, live in the rivers and lakes.

Africa has massive mountain ranges. Along the north-west coast stretches the 4 000 m high chain of the Atlas Mountains, and the tallest peak of the Ethiopian Highlands in the north-east is 4 620 m high. In the east, near the great African lakes, the tallest mountains of the continent soar to over 5 000 m.

There are also high mountains in West Africa. Mt. Cameroon, the biggest mountain in the country of Cameroon, is 4 070 m high, and is still an active volcano. Along the south-east coast of Africa there is another chain of tall mountains, the Drakensberg Mountains, more than 3 000 m high. Many species of animals live among the forests and rocky slopes of the African mountains.

In the western part of the Indian Ocean, to the south-east of Africa, there are a number of islands. The largest of these, Madagascar, is notable for its flora and fauna, some of which can be found nowhere else in the world. There are several small archipelagoes close to Madagascar—the Seychelles, Comoro Islands and Mascarene Islands—which also have their own interesting animals.

The Savannahs and Plains

The African savannahs do not look the same everywhere. Some are covered in sparse forests, especially of acacia trees and oil palms, while the most typical trees are the huge baobabs, which grow singly, a long way apart. Another type of savannah is covered in shrubs, and one typical feature of all the savannahs is the termite mounds, which may be up to several metres high.

In areas where the rainy seasons come twice a year, the grass often grows very tall. Elephant grass reaches a height of 2 to 3 m, and many other species reach an average height of 2 m. In the drier savannah regions the grass is short. During the dry season there are often huge fires in these grasslands, but when the rains return the countryside soon becomes green again.

Parts of Africa with a dry season lasting seven to nine months are covered by dry plains. There the grass grows no higher than 1 m, and typical plants are low, thorny bushes and succulents, which are able to store water in their flesh for long periods.

Photograph by Jan Jeník

9

Forest Areas

Rainforests are found particularly in West Africa, where rainfall is regular and heavy. It is always damp and hot in the forests, so jungle plants grow very vigorously, and the treetops form such a dense roof overhead that the sun's rays can scarcely penetrate. The animals of the tropical rainforest are well adapted to life in the constant half-light.

Rainforests are complex communities of plants and animals. For example, botanists have identified more than 3 000 plant species, including more than a thousand kinds of tree from many different species, in the same forest. Rainforests are less dense around the edges than in the middle, and that is where most of the animals live because there is more light.

The best-known trees of the African jungle are the mahogany, various species of the genus *Ficus* and oil palms. The trees of the genus *Cola* are especially famous, for their large seeds are used to make Coca Cola.

Photograph by Jan Jeník

Rivers, Lakes and Swamps

Some parts of Africa—the deserts, plains and savannahs—suffer from drought, but there are also extensive areas with plenty of water. During the dry season, life centres on the water sources—rivers, water-holes and lakes, though the main year-round sources of water are the mountains and tropical rainforests, from which the continent's mightiest rivers spring.

The rivers and lakes of Africa are richly populated with fish, and also provide a home for those typical African water reptiles, the crocodiles, as well as being vitally important in the life of one large mammal—the hippopotamus.

The waters of some shallow lakes, such as Lake Nakuru in Kenya, contain a high percentage of salt.

In the areas surrounding the rivers and lakes there are often extensive swamps, whose typical form of vegetation is reeds, and in the basin of the White Nile papyrus grows—this was used to make writing scrolls in ancient times.

Photograph by Jan Jeník

Mountainous and Rocky Areas

Many highland and mountainous regions of Africa are wooded, particularly in West and East Africa, where forests can be found growing up to heights of more than 4 000 m. Many animal species make their homes in these woods, and even above the tree-line the mountains teem with life. In the high-altitude pastures animals live right up to the ice-cap. Kilimanjaro, in East Africa, the continent's highest mountain, is a typical example.

On the steep mountain slopes alpine plants and shrubs blossom all year, attracting large numbers of insects. These in turn provide food for many insect-eating birds and other animals.

The tall rocks which rise up in many places out of the bush are inhabited by animals which are specially adapted to life in such an environment, mainly hyraxes and some species of reptiles. But they regularly share their rocky homes with other animals, such as birds of prey, or even lions, which occasionally go there to seek shelter for their young among the natural caves and crevices to be found there.

Photograph by Bořivoj Záruba

Deserts and Semideserts

Deserts and semideserts are a characteristic feature of the African landscape. The largest and most famous desert in the world, the Sahara, is situated in the north of the continent, and most of its ground consists of bare sand, clay or stones. Desert vegetation is sparse, never forming a continuous cover, though even here low bushes grow in places, especially the thorny *Alhagi maurorum* with its beautiful red flowers.

In spite of the harsh conditions in the Sahara, many creatures live there, including large antelopes. The animals get most of their vital water supplies from the juicy leaves of succulents, but during the day most of them hide away deep in the ground, since the temperature often rises to over 50° C.

Oases are a typical feature of the deserts. These are places where underground water rises to the surface, providing suitable conditions for vegetable and animal life, and shelter for the human inhabitants of the desert.

Photograph by Bořivoj Záruba

Madagascar

The island of Madagascar lies off the south-east coast of Africa, with the Indian Ocean lying in between. Its flora and fauna are unusually distinctive.

The most remarkable of the animals there are the lemurs which, like the insect-eating tenrecs, are only found on Madagascar. This large island is also the home of a number of species of iguanas and large boas which are typically American, and which occur nowhere else in Africa. This indicates that in prehistoric times Madagascar was joined to America.

The plant life of Madagascar is extremely varied, and there are many species which are not found anywhere else in the world. There are several hundred species of orchid, and botanists continue to find new varieties. Ferns are numerous, and hundreds of species of vine twine round the tall trees.

However, in the past large areas of the forests of Madagascar were cut down and burnt, destroying many species of plant and making it difficult to form a complete picture of the island's flora today.

AFRICA

MAMMALS

Aardvark
Antelope, Cape Eland
Antelope, Giant Eland
Antelope, Sable
Aoudad or Barbary Sheep
Ass, African Wild
Aye-aye

Baboon, Anubis
Baboon, Gelada
Baboon, Sacred or Hamadryas
Badger, Honey or Ratel
Beisa or East African Oryx
Buffalo, Cape
Bushbaby, Senegal

Cat, African Wild or Caffer
Cheetah
Chimpanzee

Dassie or Rock Hyrax
Dog, African Wild
Drill
Duiker, Grey

Elephant, African

Fossa
Fox, Fennec

Gazelle, Grant's
Gazelle, Thomson's
Gemsbok, True
Gerenuk
Giraffe
Gnu, Brindled
Gorilla
Guereza, Mantled

Hartebeest, Bastard
Hartebeest, Common
Hippopotamus
Hippopotamus, Pygmy
Hog, River

Hyaena, Brown
Hyaena, Spotted or Laughing
Hyrax, Rock or Dassie

Impala
Indri

Jackal, Common or Golden

Kudu, Greater

Lemur, Mongoose
Lemur, Ring-tailed
Lemur, Ruffed
Leopard
Lion

Mandrill
Meerkat, Slender-tailed or Suricate
Monkey, De Brazza's
Monkey, Grass or Green

Nyala, Lowland

Okapi
Oribi
Oryx, East African or Beisa
Oryx, Scimitar-horned

Pangolin, Giant
Porcupine, Crested
Potto

Ratel or Honey Badger
Rhinoceros, Black or Hooked-lipped
Rhinoceros, White or Square-lipped

Serval
Sheep, Barbary or Aoudad
Situtunga
Springbok
Suricate or Slender-tailed Meerkat

Tenrec, Common

Wart-hog
Waterbuck, Defassa

Zebra, Grévy's
Zebra, Mountain
Zebra, Steppe

BIRDS

Bee-eater, Carmine
Bee-eater, Red-throated
Bishop, Orange
Bustard, Black-bellied
Bustard, Kori

Crane, Royal

Eagle, African Fish
Eagle, Bateleur
Eagle, Congo Serpent
Eagle, Crowned
Eagle, Verreaux's

Flamingo, Lesser
Francolin, Hildebrandt's

Gallinule, Allen's
Goshawk, Dark Chanting
Guineafowl, Common or Tufted
Guineafowl, Vulturine

Hammerhead
Hawk, Long-tailed
Honeyguide, Black-throated
Hornbill, African Ground

Ibis, Hermit or Waldrapp
Ibis, Sacred

Jacana, African or Lily-trotter

Kingfisher, Pied

Lily-trotter or African Jaçana
Lovebird, Lilian's
Lovebird, Masked
Lovebird, Red-headed
Lovebird, Rosy-faced or Rose-ringed

Mousebird, Blue-naped

Nightjar, Pennant-wing

Ostrich
Owl, Cape Eagle
Owl, Spotted Eagle
Owl, White-faced Scops

Parakeet, Rose-ringed
Parrot, African Grey
Parrot, Brown-necked
Parrot, Jardine's
Parrot, Meyer's
Parrot, Red-bellied
Parrot, Vassa
Parrot, Yellow-billed Senegal
Peacock, Congo
Pigeon, Bruce's Green

Roller, Abyssinian
Roller, Lilac-breasted

Secretary Bird
Shoebill or Whale-headed Stork
Spurfowl, Red-necked
Stork, Marabou
Stork, Whale-headed or Shoebill

Vulture, African Lappet-faced
Vulture, Egyptian

Waldrapp or Hermit Ibis
Widowbird, Paradise

REPTILES

Chameleon, Common
Cobra, Black-necked Spitting
Cobra, Egyptian
Crocodile, Nile

Gecko, Malagasy

Python, African

Skink, Common

Tortoise, Giant
Tortoise, Tornier's

Viper, Gaboon
Viper, Horned
Viper, Saw-scaled

AMPHIBIANS

Toad, African Clawed

Toad Bufo mauretanicus

FISH

Bichir Polypterus bichir

Cichlid Labeotropheus fuelleborni
Cichlid Pseudotropheus zebra

Cichlid, Red or Jewel Fish
Cyprinodont Aphyosemion gardneri
Cyprinodont Aphyosemion sjostedti

Fish, Butterfly
Fish, Jewel or Red Cichlid

Killifish Epiplatys annulatus

Lungfish Protopterus dolloi
Lyretail, Red

Mormyrid Gnathonemus petersi
Mouthbrooder, Mozambique
Mudskipper Periophthalmus
    koelreuteri

Perch, Climbing Ctenopoma
    fasciolatum

Silverfish, Sebae

INVERTEBRATES

Beetle, Goliath

Locust, Desert

Scarab, Sacred
Scorpion Buthus occitanus
Scorpion, West African
Spider Eresus niger
Stick Insect, Mediterranean

16

THE
SAVANNAHS
AND
PLAINS

Uganda/Sudan — savannah

MAMMALS

SENEGAL BUSHBABY
Galago senegalensis

This small primate inhabits bushy tracts of savannah where there are occasional trees and sparse woodlands. Its body is only 15 cm long, while its hairy tail measures 20 cm. The Senegal Bushbaby leaps nimbly from branch to branch, and on the ground it jumps up to 2 m at a time. It feeds mainly on insects, especially beetles, which it catches in its hands. It also likes sweet fruit, and sometimes tears off green shoots and blossoms. During the day it hides in the hollows of trees, especially giant baobabs, setting out in search of food only after dark. Individuals or families defend their own territory, marking it out with their urine.

At the end of the dry season the female has one or two young, which she carries around on her stomach or her back.

SACRED or HAMADRYAS BABOON
Papio hamadryas

The Sacred or Hamadryas Baboon lives in the savannahs of south-east Ethiopia and northern Somalia. The male weighs about 35 kg, though females reach only half that size. These sturdy apes live in large groups, always led by the strongest of the males, and during the day they wander about rocky areas of the savannah in search of food. Sacred Baboons are omnivorous, eating juicy fruit, berries, shoots and roots, but also liking to hunt small mammals, up to the size of a hare, and sometimes even preying on baby antelopes. Around midday the baboons visit water-holes, returning in the late afternoon to their regular sleeping-quarters among the rocks. They spend the night in caves, where it is difficult for their predators, mainly leopards, to attack them.

Usually a single offspring, or occasionally twins, is born. The new-born baboons cling tightly to their mother's breast, but when they are older they ride on her back.

Senegal Bushbaby

Sacred or Hamadryas Baboon

Grass or Green Monkey

GRASS or GREEN MONKEY
Cercopithecus aethiops

The Grass or Green Monkey is found throughout western, eastern and southern Africa. It inhabits wooded or bushy savannahs and the edges of forests. Its body reaches a length of 45—65 cm and its tail 45—70 cm. It lives in small troops of 6—20 animals, and searches for food both in trees and on the ground. They pick various fruits, bite off shoots, peel off bark, collect fallen seeds and pull up roots, often entering fruit plantations where they do a great deal of damage. They also eat insects and larvae, and may attack small birds and mammals. They are hunted by leopards, large birds of prey and baboons.

The female gives birth to a single offspring, which she carries at her breast.

COMMON or GOLDEN JACKAL
Canis aureus

The Common or Golden Jackal is one of the best-known canine carnivores. It is mostly found in Africa, but also in Asia Minor and India. It lives in open and woodland savannahs, and in semidesert regions. It reaches a height of about 40 cm at the shoulders and weighs up to 9 kg. The Common Jackal usually lives in pairs or in family groups. It is a nocturnal creature, normally going out to hunt rodents, hares, lizards and snakes after dark. It is adept at catching scorpions, and also likes to eat sweet, fallen fruit. At night, it sometimes approaches human settlements, stealing poultry and eggs from outbuildings. When jackals come across lions devouring prey they will hang about and wait for the left-overs.

The jackal digs itself a lair up to 1.5 m deep

Common or Golden Jackal

African Wild Dog

20

Honey Badger or Ratel

among the bushes, where it shelters through the day, and where the female gives birth to 6—9 young.

AFRICAN WILD DOG
Lycaon pictus

The African Wild Dog is widespread over almost all African savannahs. This canine carnivore is powerfully built, standing 75 cm tall at the shoulders and sometimes weighing more than 30 kg. The dogs hunt in packs, and few creatures are safe from attack. African Wild Dogs join forces to chase and kill antelopes and other large hoofed mammals. They have great speed and stamina, and are exceptionally savage — even leopards and lions are wary of them. The pack of 10—20 dogs is led by the strongest male, the other members being subordinate to him.

In a lair dug out of the ground, the female usually gives birth to 5—7 young. The whole pack brings pieces of meat from the prey to feed nursing mothers.

HONEY BADGER or RATEL
Mellivora capensis

The Honey Badger, or Ratel, is a member of the weasel family, found in savannahs and forests throughout almost the whole of Afri-

ca south of the Sahara. It weighs up to 11 kg, and lives either singly or in pairs. Honey Badgers sleep in burrows dug in the ground, which may be more than 2 m deep. They are omnivorous, hunting small mammals, catching invertebrates, sucking birds' eggs and eating sweet fruit, but their favourite foods are the honey and larvae of wild bees. The Honey Badger even climbs trees to get at bees' nests. It is often led to these nests by the Honeyguide, a small bird which attracts the attention of the Honey Badger with a noise made by vibrating its tail feathers. The Honey Badger tears the bees' nest apart with its powerful claws, and the Honeyguide is able to eat what is left over.

The young are usually born to the female in an underground burrow.

SURICATE or SLENDER-TAILED MEERKAT
Suricata suricatta

The Suricate, or Slender-tailed Meerkat, is a small civet-like carnivore which lives in

21

southern Africa in the dry steppes or on forest edges. Suricates are very gregarious, living in colonies of 20 or more throughout the year. They dig out burrows with their strong claws, or sometimes take up residence in caves among the rocks. They hunt in the area around their lairs, catching insects, scorpions, spiders and small vertebrates, mostly birds, rodents and reptiles. They attack the strongly poisonous cobra, being highly resistant to its venom, and also eat fallen fruit and berries.

The 2—4 young born to the female Suricate are blind for about the first 12 days of their life.

SPOTTED or LAUGHING HYAENA
Crocuta crocuta

The Spotted or Laughing Hyaena lives in the savannahs and semideserts of Africa. It is a powerful carnivore, reaching a height of up to 90 cm at the shoulders and weighing up to 80 kg. During the day it usually shelters in underground lairs or dark caves. After dark, pairs or small groups of these hyaenas set out in search of prey, attacking antelopes and their young, and domestic animals such as goats, sheep and calves. Hyaenas like to follow lions around as they hunt, later eating what is left of their prey, and their extremely strong jaws can crush even the long bones of large animals.

The female digs a lair 1 m deep and 2 m long. Her litter usually contains 1—2 pups, but sometimes as many as 4, which are born well-developed with their eyes open.

BROWN HYAENA
Hyaena brunnea

The Brown Hyaena is a native of South Africa, living in dry, bushy savannahs. It is up to 80 cm tall at the shoulders, and weighs around 55 kg. Like other hyaenas, it is nocturnal. During the day it stays in caves or underground lairs, going in search of prey after sunset. It prefers to feed on the carcasses of large animals, but also hunts live prey, mainly young antelope. When it can find nothing better it will also catch frogs and reptiles, or even eat soft fallen fruit.

The female gives birth to 2—4 pups.

Spotted or Laughing Hyaena

Brown Hyaena

Serval

African Wild Cat or Caffer Cat

AFRICAN WILD CAT or CAFFER CAT
Felis sylvestris libyca

The African Wild Cat or Caffer Cat is found in all types of African savannah. During the day this carnivore, which may weigh more than 6 kg, hides away in thickets of shrubs. In rocky areas it will shelter in caves, hunting for food only after dark. Its main prey is birds, especially guineafowl, and it also hunts small mammals and reptiles, sometimes visiting human settlements in the night and making off with hens or ducks.

The litter contains 2—5 kittens, which are born blind and can see at 9—11 days.

The African Wild Cat is an ancestor of the domestic cat. In ancient Egypt it was regarded as a sacred animal, its embalmed body being placed in tombs.

SERVAL
Felis serval

The Serval is a long-legged feline carnivore which grows to a height of about 55 cm at the shoulders, weighs 13—18 kg and is found in savannahs and the outskirts of sparse forests. It hunts mainly in the evening and at night, feeding on birds, hares, reptiles and locusts, and sometimes catching fish in shallow waters or stealing poultry from native settlements.

The Serval has a litter of 2—4 young, born in the underground lairs left by aardvarks. They are blind at birth, being able to see after 9 days.

LION
Panthera leo

The Lion is the largest of the African carnivores. The male, usually identifiable by his huge mane, stands up to 100 cm tall at the shoulders and weighs 225 kg, though the female, who has no mane, is smaller. The Lion's usual habitat is savannah with scattered trees, but it is also found on the edges of semidesert areas. However, Lions always live near a source of water so they can drink regularly.

Lions form family groups called prides, led by the strongest male, which often hunt together. Their most frequent prey is antelope and zebra, but they do not hunt every day. The herds know when lions are not hungry and they may graze safely. When hunting, the Lion may lie in wait at a water-hole or stalk its chosen prey, or the pride will round up animals, then if a large animal is killed

Lion

24

the whole family will feed off it. A hungry adult eats 20 kg or more of meat at a time, though it will not usually eat again for three days. When it has eaten its fill, it rests in the shade, sometimes lying on a convenient tree trunk. A pride of lions does not have a regular territory, but follows the herds around; however, the leader informs other lions with his huge roar, audible up to 8 km away, that a particular hunting-ground is occupied. During the mating season the males fight over the females. A lioness gives birth to between 2 and 6 cubs under cover of bushes or in a cave. The cubs are blind, and can see after 10 days. During the first three weeks the lioness does not leave her young, food being brought to her by the male.

LEOPARD
Panthera pardus

The Leopard is widespread in Africa, and is also found in Asia. In Africa it lives mainly in the savannahs, as well as in forests and rocky areas. It is a strong, cat-like carnivore, 70 cm tall at the shoulders and weighing up to 80 kg. Black Leopards, usually called Panthers, are common. The Leopard leads a solitary life, forming pairs only for a short time in the mating season. This big cat hunts mainly at night, lying low in the daytime in caves, the hollows of huge baobabs, or the crowns of trees. It often drags even large prey up into trees, out of the reach of scavenging hyaenas, and usually attacks antelope, hogs and baboons. It will occasionally steal a goat or sheep from a pen, and also catches guineafowl; if food is in short supply it will make do with frogs or fish caught in shallow waters. Leopards leap down from trees on to their prey, or chase it for short distances at high speed.

The female gives birth to between 1 and 5 cubs in the shelter of a dense thicket or rocky hollow.

CHEETAH
Acinonyx jubatus

The Cheetah belongs to the family of Big Cats, but differs from other members in its long, thin legs and non-retractile claws. This makes it extremely well-adapted for life in the vast savannahs, where successful hunting depends on great running speed. The Cheetah is the fastest mammal on earth, reaching a speed of up to 110 km per hour over short distances, so it can catch up with

Leopard

Cheetah

an antelope or hare in the space of a few seconds. In long grass it also attacks various fowl.

Cheetahs grow to a height of 80 cm at the shoulder and weigh 45—65 kg. The litter contains between 1 and 6 young, which up to the age of 10 weeks have retractile claws which enable them to climb trees in order to hide from hyaenas.

GIANT PANGOLIN
Manis gigantea

The Giant Pangolin, up to 150 cm long, inhabits the savannahs and forest borders of West and equatorial Africa. It lives on the ground, usually close to water, hiding during the day in deep burrows which it digs with its huge claws. After dark it roams its territory in search of termite nests, using its chisel-like claws to tear these apart, then feeding on the insects. When threatened it rolls into a ball to protect its soft stomach, which is not covered, like the rest of its body, with thick scales.

The Giant Pangolin lives alone or in pairs. A single offspring is born in the underground burrow, which is approached by a very long tunnel. The young are born with their eyes open.

Giant Pangolin

CRESTED PORCUPINE
Hystrix galeata

The Crested Porcupine is found in bushy and wooded savannahs throughout East Africa. It grows up to 85 cm long, weighing more than 20 kg. It digs itself a lair some 2 m deep, or sometimes makes its home in a rock crevice. The animals live in pairs or family groups, staying in their lairs in the daytime, then setting out to find food after

Crested Porcupine

dark. They eat fallen fruit, berries, roots, shoots and seeds.

The female has 2—4 young in a deep burrow. They are born with soft spines, which begin to harden after 10 days.

AARDVARK
Orycteropus afer

The Aardvark lives in savannahs and sparse forests throughout the whole of Africa. It grows up to 60 cm tall at the shoulders, reaching a weight of about 80 kg. It has conspicuously long ears and massive spade-like claws, which it uses to dig a burrow up to 6 m deep, with many tunnels and exits. It spends the day sleeping in this underground maze, setting out to forage in the evening. It looks for termite nests, demolishing their strong earth walls with its great claws. It then picks up the termites, its chief food, using its tongue. An Aardvark will visit several termite nests in the course of a single night.

Offspring are born singly, and at the age of only two weeks accompany their mothers on their nightly foraging trips.

BLACK or HOOKED-LIPPED RHINOCEROS
Diceros bicornis

The sturdy Black Rhinoceros can be found in much of the dry, bushy savannahs of East, Central and South-east Africa. It grows to a height of 150 cm at the shoulders and

Aardvark

Black or Hooked-lipped Rhinoceros

weighs up to 1—1.5 tonnes. The Black Rhinoceros is a solitary creature, each one having its own territory which is marked out with droppings. Only in the mating season do the males seek a partner, and a single young is born after a gestation period of 17—18 months. Then the mother follows her calf around everywhere, caring for the young for several years. If another offspring is born, the older calf walks behind the younger, and so the family keeps together. Black Rhinoceroses travel along well-trodden tracks, about 50 cm wide. They search for food in the early morning or at dusk, feeding on twigs and leaves from bushes and small trees. They usually visit

28

White or Square-lipped Rhinoceros

water-holes, sometimes more than 20 km away across the savannah, in the evening, and they like to wallow in mud. Despite its colossal size, a charging Black Rhinoceros may reach a speed of 50 km per hour.

WHITE or SQUARE-LIPPED RHINOCEROS
Ceratotherium simum

The White Rhinoceros is the largest African animal after the elephant, growing up to 180 cm at the shoulders and weighing 3.5—5 tonnes. It is found in the bushy savannahs and grassy plains of northern and southern Africa, and is more gregarious than the Black Rhinoceros, living in family groups of 5—10 animals. Each of these herds has its own territory, criss-crossed by well-trodden paths. During the day these rhinoceroses keep to the shade of trees; in the early morning and evening they go out to graze.

After a 490-day gestation period a single calf is born; this follows behind its mother.

STEPPE ZEBRA
Equus burchelli

The Steppe Zebra, of which there are a number of subspecies, is distributed throughout East, South-east and South-west Africa, inhabiting bushy or partly

Steppe Zebra

wooded savannahs. It is gregarious, living in groups, and the family unit, containing several mares and their foals, is led by a strong male. The zebra's main food is grass, and the animals visit water-holes daily.

Mares give birth to a single foal, which is very active and is able to follow its mother around the next day. Zebras grow to 135 cm at the shoulders and reach a weight of 320 kg.

AFRICAN ELEPHANT
Loxodonta africana

The two types of African Elephant live in savannahs of all kinds, rainforests, mountain forests and semidesert areas. The Bush Elephant is the largest land animal in the world; it is 2.8—4 m tall at the shoulders, and weighs 3.5—6.5 tonnes. Males have tusks up to 3.4 m long, which may weigh

African Elephant

Wart-hog

more than 100 kg, though females have shorter tusks. The Forest Elephant is much smaller — 2.25—2.7 m tall at the shoulders. The elephant is a gregarious animal, living in herds of 10—50, the leader of which is an old, experienced female; old males often go off on their own. Elephants roam the countryside, browsing on grass and leaves, picking fruit or pulling down branches, stripping bark and pulling up roots. An adult elephant consumes 150—250 kg of food per day, and visits water-holes daily. They suck up water with their trunks and squirt it into their mouths, and also like to bathe, after which they fling earth or sand over themselves.

After a gestation period of 22—24 months, a single calf is born; it is 90 cm tall at birth and weighs 120 kg. The young remains with its mother for two years: throughout this period it is suckled, taking the milk directly into its mouth, though calves are able to fend for themselves after a year. Elephants are mature after 10—12 years, and have a life span of up to 65 years, a considerable age for any animal.

WART-HOG
Phacochoerus aethiopicus

The Wart-hog is a native of the African savannahs south of the Sahara, usually living near water. The male may weigh up to 115 kg, but the female is only half that size, and they live in family groups. During the day they feed on grass, shoots and leaves, or pick up fallen fruit, often wandering into cultivated fields, where they can cause considerable damage to crops. Grazing Warthogs often walk on their knees. At night they shelter in disused aardvark lairs, and here the female gives birth to 3 or 4, or sometimes up to 8, young on a bed of dry grass.

GIRAFFE
Giraffa camelopardalis

Giraffes live in savannahs that have a thickish cover of tall shrubs and trees, particularly acacias. Their height at the shoulders is 3—3.6 m, but their overall height may be more than 6 m. They live in herds which sometimes contain more than 50 animals, though old males usually live alone. Giraffes roam the countryside, stripping leaves off trees, usually acacias, with their very long tongues. Only rarely do they graze; on such occasions, like when drinking, they have to spread their legs wide in order to reach the ground.

Giraffes usually have a single off spring, though occasionally twins are born. At birth the young Giraffe can be up to 2 m tall.

CAPE ELAND ANTELOPE
Taurotragus oryx

The Cape Eland Antelope is an inhabitant of the savannahs and plains, but can also be found on the outskirts of forests, in Southeast and South Africa. It is one of the largest species of antelope, measuring up to 175 cm at the shoulders and sometimes weighing 680 kg. It can usually be found in herds of 25—70 animals, though during the dry season, when antelope migrate in search of food, these herds are larger. Cape Eland Antelope eat the leaves of bushes and trees, grass and various fruits, such as wild melons, and they also dig up roots and tubers with their hooves. They go to watering places daily. On only the second day after its birth the young will follow its mother to join the herd.

In some parts of Africa attempts are being made to domesticate the Cape Eland Antelope, for it is far more resistant to disease than the African breeds of domestic cattle.

Giraffe

Cape Eland Antelope

SABLE ANTELOPE
Hippotragus niger

The Sable Antelope is found throughout Central and South-east Africa, in dry, bushy or thinly-forested savannahs. It is a sturdily-built species, 140 cm tall at the shoulders and weighing up to 250 kg. The male has huge horns, which can grow up to 165 cm long. The female, which has dark chestnut colouring, carries a pair of thinner and shorter horns. Sable Antelope go about in small herds of 10—20 animals. They mostly eat grass, but sometimes also strip the leaves off bushes. The young, which are fawn in colour, are born singly.

BASTARD HARTEBEEST
Damaliscus dorcas

The Bastard Hartebeest lives in the savannahs and plains of South Africa. It is 100 cm tall at the shoulders, weighing up to 80 kg, and is conspicuous for its lyre-shaped horns which grow up to 50 cm long. These

hartebeests live in herds of 6—30 animals, several of which join forces during the dry season to go in search of food. They mostly eat grass, visiting watering places regularly, usually towards evening. In the shelter of tall grass the female gives birth to a single young.

Sable Antelope

33

Bastard Hartebeest

BRINDLED GNU
Connochaetes taurinus

The Brindled Gnu is one of the most abundant antelopes. It is found mostly in East Africa, though its area of distribution stretches as far as Angola, and it inhabits grassy and bushy savannahs and sparse forests. It grows to a height of 140 cm at the shoulders and weighs 160—270 kg. Brindled Gnus are very gregarious, living in large herds, but within the herd there are smaller groups comprising several females and a single male, who guards his mates and defends a small territory. The animals make long migrations in search of food, sometimes over 1 500 km every year, when herds may number several thousand head. Such a large number of antelopes would not be able to find enough food in one place. The Brindled Gnu feeds mainly on grass, grazing for most of the day. When possible

Brindled Gnu

it visits watering places daily, but can also go up to 5 days without water if necessary. During the dry season it gets part of its water requirement from eating succulents and wild melons.

The female gives birth to 1 or occasionally 2 young. The main enemies of gnus are lions, but hyaenas often attack their young.

GIANT ELAND ANTELOPE
Taurotragus derbianus

The Giant Eland Antelope is distributed in the western and central parts of the continent, from Senegal to southern Sudan. It has been overhunted in many places and is now classed as an endangered species. It lives in woodland savannahs and thin forests, always near water. It is the largest of all the living antelopes, standing up to 175 cm at the shoulders, and weighing 450—900 kg. It has powerful spirally twisted horns measuring up to 1 metre.

The Giant Eland Antelope is a gregarious herbivore.

LOWLAND NYALA
Tragelaphus angasi

The Lowland Nyala is indigenous to the plains and bushland of South Africa. It is

Giant Eland Antelope

a slenderly built antelope, 105 cm tall at the shoulders, and weighing 100—125 kg. The bull's horns are about 80 cm long, but the cow is hornless and is more finely built. Nyalas usually live in small herds consisting of one adult bull and several cows with up to 30 young of various ages. They are very active both by day and night, coming out to graze late in the afternoon and continuing until morning. During the day, they rest among the bushes. They feed mainly on leaves, twigs, fruit and grass, visiting the water-holes regularly.

Lowland Nyala

♂

♀

35

True Gemsbok

Beisa
or East African Oryx

TRUE GEMSBOK
Oryx gazella gazella

The True Gemsbok lives on dry plains, semideserts and open savannahs in the western part of South Africa. It is a robust antelope, up to 120 cm tall at the shoulders, and weighing 205 kg. The horns reach about 120 cm in males, though they are a little shorter and more delicate in females. The Gemsbok is a gregarious antelope, only the old bulls becoming solitary. The remainder live in herds 30—40 strong, and gather in hundreds when migrating to find food

during the dry season. The steppe grass is the mainstay of their diet. After 270 days of gestation, a single young is born.

BEISA or EAST AFRICAN ORYX
Oryx gazella beisa

The Beisa, or East African Oryx, is native to the dry open savannahs of East Africa, which are covered by bushes and short grass. The horns may be up to 1 m long, though the average length is 75 cm. The female has slightly shorter and finer horns than the male.

The Beisa lives in small herds of 6—40, often together with zebras or other antelopes. Old bulls are usually solitary. Beisas feed mainly on tough grass, twigs and the leaves of thorny bushes. They regularly visit water-holes even though they can go for several days without water.

ORIBI
Ourebia ourebi

The Oribi is a small antelope of grassland

Oribi

Common Hartebeest

Gerenuk

savannahs and plains south of the Sahara. It reaches 50—65 cm at the shoulder and weighs 9—20 kg. The male has short, thin, straight horns about 15 cm long. The female lacks horns. Several subspecies of this small antelope are known, and are considered by some zoologists to be independent species.

Oribis live in pairs or in small groups of 5—10, rarely forming larger herds.

COMMON HARTEBEEST
Alcelaphus buselaphus

The Common Hartebeest is widespread in an area from Senegal to Ethiopia, and to central Tanzania. It prefers open, or sometimes thinly wooded, savannahs. It is 120—145 cm tall and weighs 125—200 kg. The Common Hartebeest forms small groups, usually with 4—15, but sometimes up to 30 members. Herds of thousands used to roam the savannahs, but man has mercilessly hunted this antelope, sometimes to the point of extinction. In East Africa it lives together with zebras.

GERENUK
Litocranius walleri

The Gerenuk lives in areas of dry bush and semideserts in Ethiopia, Somalia, Tanzania and Kenya. It stands 90—105 cm tall at the shoulder and weighs 35—50 kg. The females lack horns. It is one of the few species of antelope to have increased over the last few decades.

The Gerenuk is solitary, or forms small groups of 5—7 members, pairing off in the rutting season.

IMPALA
Aepyceros melampus

The Impala is native to East Africa, mainly south of the equator, and ranges to southern Mozambique and westwards to Angola. It stands 80—95 cm at the shoulder and weighs 45—80 kg. The female is more slenderly built and has no horns.

Impala form large herds of 100 or more. When pursued, they run very quickly, making extraordinary leaps, 10 m long and as much as 3 m high.

Impala

Springbuck

THOMSON'S GAZELLE
Gazella thomsoni

Thomson's Gazelle is found in East Equatorial Africa, in grassland, open plains and in savannahs covered by tall grass and thick brushwood. It is the most abundant gazelle in this part of Africa, occurring in two subspecies. It measures 65 cm at the shoulder and weighs 20—30 kg. The male has horns approximately 30 cm long, but the female has only small horns. This gazelle usually lives in herds of 10—50.

SPRINGBOK
Antidorcas marsupialis

The Springbok is a resident of open dry savannahs and plains of South and southwestern Africa. It is 75—85 cm tall at the shoulder and weighs 32—36 kg. Its lyreshaped horns measure 40 cm on average. It is a characteristic antelope of South Africa. When alarmed, the herd flees in long, high leaps.

Thomson's Gazelle

Grey Duiker

The Springbok is a highly gregarious animal, moving in numerous herds. In many places they have been exterminated because of the enormous amount of damage done to farmland. Water-holes are visited regularly.

GREY DUIKER
Sylvicapra grimmia

The Grey Duiker inhabits a large part of the African continent. In the north, the area of its distribution is bordered by the Sahara Desert. Duikers live in the bush, on plains and desert margins, and in the mountains up to the snowline. It is one of the smaller antelope species, reaching 50—65 cm at the shoulders, and weighing only 10—14 kg. Several subspecies are distinguished.
The single young Duiker stays with its mother for over 7 months, and then begins to fend for itself.

GRANT'S GAZELLE
Gazella granti

In the bushy savannahs and semidesert regions of Equatorial Africa the slender Grant's Gazelle may be found. It is 80—90 cm tall at the shoulders and weighs 45—80 kg. The horns of the male may be 80 cm long, while the female's are shorter. These gazelles live in small groups of 6—30, and the herd is led by a strong male. They roam from place to place grazing and eating the leaves of bushes, visiting watering places irregularly, for they can go a whole week without water.
One, or more rarely two, young may be born to the female at any time of the year. These stay in the shelter of long grass or bushes for several days before following their mothers to join the herd.

Grant's Gazelle

CAPE BUFFALO
Syncerus caffer caffer

The Cape Buffalo is a huge animal, reaching a height of 170 cm at the shoulders and a weight of 820 kg. Its horns are also extremely thick and up to 160 cm long. The Cape Buffalo lives in large herds in the broad African savannahs. The ruler of the herd is a giant bull, but its leader is an experienced cow. Old males live in solitude or form their own groups. During the day buffalo rest in thick vegetation close to water or wallow in mud. At night they graze, eating leaves and twigs. They drink frequently, so they are always to be found near water.
Females give birth to a single calf, which its mother looks after carefully and protects from predators. Buffalo calves have many enemies, particularly the big cats and crocodiles, but not even a lion dare attack an adult buffalo.

Cape Buffalo

BIRDS

OSTRICH
Struthio camelus

The Ostrich is the largest living bird on earth. It may be as much as 2.5 m in overall height, and an adult male weighs over 200 kg. Females, which are brown in colour, are less heavily built. The Ostrich is found in savannahs, semideserts and the edges of deserts, usually in groups of 6—8, but sometimes in flocks of several hundred. At the mating season the male runs wildly around in circles, making a gurgling sound. He is responsible for making the nesting hole in the ground, using his beak and body. The two to four females lay their creamy

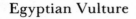
Egyptian Vulture

Ostrich

white eggs, weighing up to 1.5 kg, in the same nest, so there may be 30 or more eggs in one hollow. During the night the male sits on them, and in the daytime the females take turns. After 6 weeks the chicks hatch, and they are then looked after mainly by the father, though one of the females may help him. The young gather their own food the day after they are hatched. Ostriches eat berries, shoots and grass, insects, lizards, rodents and small birds. The Ostrich is unable to fly, though it can run at 50 km per hour, taking leaps of up to 4 m at a time.

EGYPTIAN VULTURE
Neophron percnopterus

The Egyptian Vulture, which has a wingspan of 170 cm, is found throughout almost the whole of Africa, in both savannahs and semidesert areas, and it often visits human settlements. It can usually be seen in open spaces, where it searches for carcasses which have been abandoned by other large animals. Sometimes great flocks of vultures gather at the rubbish tips of large towns, but they also hunt live prey, catching locusts in mid-air, attacking small reptiles and frogs, and often stealing the eggs of other birds. In some areas vultures break open hard ostrich eggs by dropping stones on them.

Pairs of Egyptian Vultures build their twig nests in small caves on cliffs or in trees, lining them with pieces of skin, rag, and so on. The female lays two eggs, which are white, sometimes with russet blotches. Both partners take turns at sitting on the eggs, and both carry food to the young.

Bateleur Eagle

BATELEUR EAGLE
Terathopius ecaudatus

The Bateleur Eagle is a striking bird of prey, performing various acrobatic tricks in flight. With its wingspan of 170 cm it is a very rapid flier, capable of a speed of up to 80 km per hour. The Bateleur Eagle is found in savannahs south of the Sahara. It is mainly a scavenger, living off the meat of dead animals, but it also hunts rats, squirrels, young hares and reptiles, often catching poisonous snakes.

This bird nests on the thick branches of acacia trees, 6—20 m above the ground. Both parent birds carry twigs to build the nest for more than six months, then the female lays a single egg, which she mostly incubates herself. The male sometimes assists her, and brings food for his mate. The parents feed the chick with small pieces of food until it is 40 days old, when it is able to tear up the food for itself. The young bird leaves the nest at the age of 100—125 days.

SECRETARY BIRD
Sagittarius serpentarius

Grassy savannahs with shrubs and scattered trees form the habitat of this strange-looking, long-legged bird of prey from Senegal to Somalia, and southwards as far as the Cape. It stands about 120 cm tall and has a wingspan of about 2 m. It walks through the tall grass in search of live prey, which it kills with its beak and claws. It feeds on small mammals, birds and reptiles, and is welcomed in many areas because it catches dangerous poisonous snakes. It does not tear them apart, but swallows them whole. Sometimes it also catches locusts.

Pairs of these birds build their nests at the top of trees 3—7 m above the ground, protected from the side by thick bushes. The

Secretary Bird

Common or Tufted Guineafowl

Hildebrandt's Francolin

Red-necked Spurfowl

nest is a flat construction made of twigs, which the birds bring in their beaks. The female lays 2—3 red-spotted eggs, which she incubates herself, while the male brings her food. Both parents then care for the young chicks, which are able to fly at the age of 65—85 days.

COMMON or TUFTED GUINEAFOWL
Numida meleagris

Large flocks of Common or Tufted Guineafowl roam the grassy savannahs throughout East Africa. These birds scurry about the ground, taking to the air only if danger threatens, when they make for the nearest cover with their rapid but clumsy flight. At night they roost in the branches of tall, solitary trees, and during the day they eat seeds and berries, nibble shoots, and catch insects and other invertebrates.

In the nesting season guineafowl live in pairs. The female scratches out a nest beneath a bush in the tall grass, giving it a scanty lining of leaves. She lays 6—10 eggs, which she incubates herself. At first the mother feeds the chicks, but later they are looked after by both parents.

HILDEBRANDT'S FRANCOLIN
Francolinus hildebrandti

Hildebrandt's Francolin lives mainly in eastern Zaire and Tanzania. It is a small fowl-like bird, standing up to 35 cm. The female's underparts are russet and white-spotted. Francolins prefer rocky hillsides, covered by bushes and tall grass, where they fly among the shrubs on river banks, roosting in scattered trees. During most of the year they gather in coveys of 6—12 birds.
In the nesting period, they form pairs and the sharp, loud call of the males announces the occupation of the nesting grounds. The female lays 4—8 cream-white eggs and sits on them for 25 days. The male stays near the nest and warns the female of danger.

RED-NECKED SPURFOWL
Pternistis cranchii

The Red-necked Spurfowl ranges from East Africa to southern Zimbabwe and Angola. Several subspecies, differing in colour, are known, but both sexes are identically coloured in all of them. The female builds the nest, selecting a suitable site in grass under

43

Vulturine Guineafowl

Kori Bustard

a thick shrub. The nesting depression is lined with dry grass, and 5—9 cream or chestnut-coloured eggs, sometimes with purple patches, are laid there. The hen incubates them for 26 days, while the male stays near at hand.

The Red-necked Spurfowl is a game bird and its natural enemies are mainly mammalian carnivores, raptors and large snakes.

VULTURINE GUINEAFOWL
Acryllium vulturinum

The Vulturine Guineafowl is found in the eastern parts of Africa. It is a resident of grassland savannahs, and it lives in flocks. While in search of food, several birds are always on the look-out for danger, while the others seek seeds, shoots, roots and berries, insects, larvae, worms and spiders.

In the nesting season, each pair occupies a small range. The hen builds a simple nest in a depression lined with grass and leaves, and lays 8—14 cream-coloured eggs. She sits on them for 25 days and then shares the care of the young with the cock. The chicks

fend for themselves, feeding on insects and green plants.

KORI BUSTARD
Ardeotis kori

The Kori Bustard is confined to the vast savannahs of East Africa and parts of South Africa. It is plentiful in Tanzania and Kenya. The male may weigh over 15 kg, and the female, who is much smaller, about 5.5 kg.

Black-bellied Bustard

44

No nest is built, the female merely making a scrape in the ground with her body, where she lays 2 pale greenish-brown eggs with brown spots. Several pairs of bustards may nest together. All larger carnivores and birds of prey are the enemies of bustards.

BLACK-BELLIED BUSTARD
Lissotis melanogaster

The Black-bellied Bustard is found in areas of savannahs south of the Sahara, its range reaching the northern part of Cape Province and Angola. This bustard is abundant in East Africa. The male weighs up to 3 kg, and the female is slightly smaller.

The Black-bellied Bustard usually lives in pairs, but after the fledging of the young, the birds stay in small groups. This bird is predominantly insectivorous, feeding on locusts and grasshoppers and occasionally on small lizards, but it also takes plant food. The female makes a shallow depression under a bush or in tall grass, but does not line it, and she lays 1 or 2 off-white or pale olive eggs with brown, russet and grey spots, incubating them for 25 days.

YELLOW-BILLED SENEGAL PARROT
Poicephalus senegalus

The Yellow-billed Senegal Parrot, which is about 23 cm long, is found in the wooded savannahs of West Central Africa. Except during the nesting season these birds live in small flocks, often descending on cultivated fields where they eat grain crops. They also visit fruit plantations to raid the soft, ripening fruit. In the savannahs they feed mainly on fallen seeds, berries and green shoots.

During the nesting season these parrots live in pairs. They nest in the hollows of trees, high above the ground. The nest is unlined,

Yellow-billed Senegal Parrot

and the female usually lays three eggs. She incubates these herself, then the young are fed by both parents. The young fly at the age of 9 weeks.

RED-BELLIED PARROT
Poicephalus rufiventris

The Red-bellied Parrot is an inhabitant of wooded savannahs of north-eastern Africa, chiefly in places where huge baobabs and acacias grow. It lives mainly in lowland areas, though in Ethiopia it is found in mountainous areas up to a height of 2 000 m, usually between July and September.

It lives in pairs or in family groups, rarely gathering in larger flocks. About 23 cm long, these birds are inconspicuous, timid and difficult to approach. These parrots nest in holes in trees — most frequently in the trunks of massive baobabs, as far above the ground as they can get. The female lays 2 — 3 white eggs directly on to the bottom of the hole, and the young hatch after 25 days of incubation.

Red-bellied Parrot

Rosy-faced or Rose-ringed Lovebird

ROSY-FACED or ROSE-RINGED LOVEBIRD
Agapornis roseicollis

The Rosy-faced or Rose-ringed Lovebird inhabits wooded savannahs of south-western Africa. It is 15 — 17 cm tall, and both sexes are identically coloured. This small bird lives in dry areas from lowlands to mountains at an average altitude of 1 600 m. Lovebirds live in flocks, and are both conspicuous and noisy. They feed on seeds and various fruits and visit maize fields, picking underripe grain.

In the nesting season, the pairs stay together in colonies, building nests in rocky crevices or in the huge nests of gregarious weavers, such as the Social Weaver (*Philetarius socius*). These nests are composed of many chambers, each with its own entrance.

CAPE EAGLE OWL
Bubo capensis

The Cape Eagle Owl lives mainly in the Cape savannahs, its range reaching Kenya and Ethiopia, where it occurs in several isolated sites. In mountainous areas, it is found up to 4 000 m, and is called the Mountain Eagle Owl. It stands 46 — 48 cm high and both sexes are identically coloured. The Cape Eagle Owl is solitary, only forming pairs in the breeding season. It hunts after nightfall, flying noiselessly low above the savannah, searching for small rodents running in the grass. It may occasionally kill hyraxes, fruit bats, small birds or snakes and when locusts are abundant, it feeds on them as well.

SPOTTED EAGLE OWL
Bubo africanus

The Spotted Eagle Owl is widespread throughout the African continent south of the Sahara, where it inhabits savannahs and rocky wooded sites. It is also found in eastern Arabia. It is one of the smaller eagle owls, reaching a maximum length of 40 cm. It is not possible to distinguish the sexes by

White-faced Scops Owl

Cape Eagle Owl

Spotted Eagle Owl

colour, some individuals being greyish, others reddish.

Eagle Owls are solitary, forming pairs only in the nesting period, during the dry season. Most frequently, the nest is built on the ground among rocks or on hillsides or rocky projections. Sometimes it is found in tree hollows just above the ground, and occasionally this bird may settle in nests vacated by other birds.

WHITE-FACED SCOPS OWL
Otus leucotis

The White-faced Scops Owl is abundant in bushland and wooded savannahs south of the Sahara. In West Africa it also occurs in rainforests. It is 10—24 cm tall and is characterized by its striking orange-red eyes. Both sexes are identically coloured. It is solitary, and forms pairs only in the nesting season. Unlike other owls, it is predominantly diurnal, hunting early in the morning and in the late afternoon. It flies above the savannah, catching insects, or occasionally pouncing on small vertebrates. This owl does not build a nest, but settles in the abandoned shelters of other small raptors. The female lays 4—5 white eggs.

PENNANT-WING NIGHTJAR
Semeiophorus vexillarius

The Pennant-wing Nightjar is a common inhabitant of the southern half of the continent, and when the nesting season is over it may fly north as far as Sierra Leone and the Sudan. It stands up to 30 cm high and the spring plumage of the male is particularly impressive, one pair of primaries growing into fluttering pennants up to 40 cm long, which it displays during the courtship flight.

47

Blue-naped Mousebird

Pennant-wing Nightjar

Lilac-breasted Roller

After courtship they break off, but the remains are not shed until the annual moult.

BLUE-NAPED MOUSEBIRD
Colius macrourus

The Blue-naped Mousebird ranges from Senegal eastwards to Somalia. It prefers places covered by brushwood and can be found at altitudes up to 2 000 m. It is about 33 cm long and the tail is twice as long as the body. Both sexes are identically coloured.

In the nesting period, they form pairs and build nests among the shrubs. The nest is made with fine roots, grass stalks and bark, and is lined with soft leaves. 3—4 white or yellowish-green, brown-dotted eggs are laid, and both partners take part in the incubation for 13—14 days. The chicks are naked when hatched, but soon begin to grow feathers.

LILAC-BREASTED ROLLER
Coracias caudata

The Lilac-breasted Roller is a resident of shrub-covered and woodland savannahs in South and East Africa. It also occurs on the Island of Zanzibar. It reaches a length of 35 cm, and has a forked tail. Rollers can normally be approached quite easily, but they become cautious in the nesting season, and hide with extraordinary skill. They nest in holes in trees or in termitaria.
The female lays 2—3 white eggs and sits on them from the time the first egg is laid. Incubation lasts 18—20 days and the chicks hatch over a period of several days.

ABYSSINIAN ROLLER
Coracias abyssinica

The Abyssinian Roller inhabits bushland from Senegal eastwards to Ethiopia, Uganda and Kenya, and reaches south-western

Carmine Bee-eater

Abyssinian Roller

Red-throated Bee-eater

Arabia. The body is about 40 cm long and the tail is forked. Both sexes have the same coloration. The Abyssinian Roller seeks places with tall termite mounds or solitary trees. It is fond of perching on dry twigs or in exposed places.

The female lays 4—6 white eggs and sits on them, usually alone, for 20 days. The nestlings are fed by both parents until they are able to fend for themselves. Their food ranges from large insects like locusts to small lizards, snakes and other small vertebrates.

CARMINE BEE-EATER
Merops nubicus

The Carmine Bee-eater inhabits shrub-covered savannahs near water. It ranges from Angola to Natal, but after the nesting season it migrates to Zaire and Tanzania. Carmine Bee-eaters nest in numerous colonies, pairs excavating corridors up to 1.3 m long in vertical banks, and building a nesting chamber at the end. The female lays 2—4 white eggs and both parents incubate them for 3 weeks and then feed the young. The fledglings leave the nest after 3—4 weeks and continue to be fed for another 10 days, afterwards remaining in parental company.

RED-THROATED BEE-EATER
Melittophagus bulocki

The Red-throated Bee-eater is distributed in the central part of East Africa. It flies in small flocks above the open bush, in brushwood ravines and over water. It is plentiful in some areas, notably around the Murchison Falls. It averages 22 cm in length. The Red-throated Bee-eater lives in colonies and the female lays 2—3, or occasionally 5, shiny white eggs.

African Ground Hornbill

Black-throated Honeyguide

AFRICAN GROUND HORNBILL
Bucorvus abyssinicus

Grassy and bushy savannahs with the occasional tall tree are the home of the African Ground Hornbill. This sturdy bird the size of a turkey is found across the continent from Senegal in the west to Somalia and Kenya in the east. The male has a red throat, the female a blue one. Outside the breeding season hornbills live in small groups. They mostly feed in the tall grass, deftly catching insects, lizards, snakes and small rodents with their beaks, and also eating fruit and soft berries. In the evening they fly up to roost in the branches of trees. During the nesting season Ground Hornbills form pairs. The male uses clayey earth, mixed with saliva, droppings and regurgitated food to wall his mate into a large hollow in a tree trunk. He leaves only a narrow crack through which to feed her. She lays 2 eggs, and when these have hatched the male feeds the whole family through the opening for 8—10 weeks. During that time the female moults and grows new feathers and the young are fledged. Then both parents break down the wall, and the family ends its voluntary imprisonment, which serves as protection from predators.

BLACK-THROATED HONEYGUIDE
Indicator indicator

The Black-throated Honeyguide is found in shrub-covered savannahs with occasional trees and also in thin woodland. It is well-known for leading creatures to wild bees' nests. It attracts attention with its harsh cry, then uses this to guide Honey Badgers or humans to the source of food which it has found but cannot get into. The man or animal climbs the tree and breaks into the bees' nest, taking out most of the honeycombs. The Honeyguide then takes honey and wax from the remains of the combs to-

50

Orange Bishop

Paradise Widowbird

gether with the bees' larvae. It also feeds on other species of insects and their larvae.

The Honeyguide does not build a nest. The female lays eggs in the nests of other species of birds which nest in hollows, such as barbets, woodpeckers, bee-eaters and starlings. These foster-parents hatch their eggs and rear the young.

PARADISE WIDOWBIRD
Steganura paradisea

The Paradise Widowbird is common in eastern and southern Africa, living in bushy savannahs where there are broad tracts of grass. It feeds mainly on grass seed and insects, and is a brood-parasite: the female lays her eggs in the nests of other birds, mainly those of the genus *Pytilia*. These birds then incubate the Paradise Widowbird's eggs and rear its young. One subspecies of this widowbird, living on the western border of its distribution range, has been seen to build its own nest of grass and incubate its eggs.

ORANGE BISHOP
Euplectes franciscanus

The Orange Bishop inhabits grassy savannahs and plains from Senegal to Ethiopia, Uganda and Kenya. It is 11—12 cm in length, and during the mating season the male is arrayed in splendid feathers. Orange Bishops are gregarious and nest in large colonies: each male in the colony rules over a small territory and has 3 or 4 females. He makes them spherical nests from long blades of grass and strips of bark which are placed on small branches of trees or tall bushes. The female then lines the nest and lays 2—4 blue eggs in it. She incubates these herself, and is also responsible for looking after the young. The Orange Bishop feeds mainly on grass seed and also on insects.

REPTILES

COMMON CHAMELEON
Chamaeleo chamaeleon

The Common Chameleon lives in North Africa and along the Mediterranean coast. It can be found in shrub-covered areas and also in parks and gardens. The Chameleon is up to 30 cm long, and is noted for its ability to change its colour or shade when affected by external stimuli such as light or temperature, or internal stimuli like excitement or fear. It lives in bushes, and to catch its prey it crawls hesitantly along branches or lies in wait without moving. If an insect settles nearby, the Chameleon shoots out its long, sticky tongue and catches its victim instantly.

The female lays 20—35 eggs, which are covered with a soft, leathery skin. She places them in a hole dug in the earth beneath a bush, covering the clutch with leaves and earth. The young are born after 10 weeks, and crawl away at once into the nearby bushes.

Common Chameleon

AFRICAN PYTHON
Python sebae

The African Python lives in the savannahs and sparse forests of tropical Africa. It is

African Python

Gaboon Viper

one of the largest snakes, sometimes growing to a length of more than 6 m. These
pythons are mainly nocturnal. During the
day they lie hidden in the bushes, hunting
for food after nightfall. They prey on hares,
rats, guineafowl and bustards, and the biggest pythons will even kill a young antelope.
They swallow their victims whole after
squeezing them to death.

In a sheltered spot in the hollow of a tree
the female lays up to 100 eggs with leathery
covers; she then winds her body round
them. This is both to protect them from
enemies and to keep up their temperature,
incubating them. The young snakes hatch
after 80 days, and are able to fend for themselves immediately.

GABOON VIPER
Bitis gabonica

The Gaboon Viper is found mainly in the
savannahs of the equatorial region of Central and East Africa. It is a large snake,
reaching a length of 180 cm and a weight
of 9 kg, and its venom fangs may be up to
5 cm long. Its venom glands contain large
amounts of poison, so its bite is very
dangerous, though fortunately it is not an
aggressive creature. During the day the
Gaboon Viper hides under large stones or
tree trunks, setting out to hunt after dark,
when it feeds mainly on small mammals.
The female gives birth to 10—15 live young
at a time.

INVERTEBRATES

DESERT LOCUST
Schistocerca gregaria

Locusts are found in grassy savannahs and
plains. The female grows up to 7 cm long,
with a wingspan of over 15 cm, though the
male is 1 cm smaller. The female lays
40—100 eggs at a time in the earth, and
10—12 such broods a year. The lárvae shed
their skins six times before reaching adult-
hood and becoming winged, then clouds of
locusts set off in search of food. A swarm
may contain as many as 200 000 insects,
which eat every plant in their path. In pre-
vious times locusts literally covered vast
areas of crops, often bringing famine on
those regions.

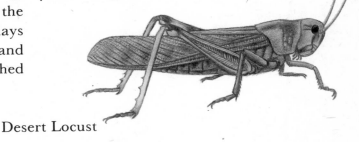

Desert Locust

Photograph by Jan Jeník

Ivory Coast

FOREST AREAS

MAMMALS

POTTO
Perodicticus potto

The Potto is found in the rainforests of Equatorial Africa, from Sierra Leone to western Kenya. They are 30—40 cm long and weigh up to 1.5 kg; they belong to the loris family of primates. Pottos live singly, coming together only in the mating season. After a 6-month gestation period the female gives birth to a single young in the hollow of a tree; she carries it on her stomach.

Pottos are mainly nocturnal. They crawl slowly along branches looking for juicy fruit, but are omnivorous, and catch insects and like to eat the eggs or young of birds.

GORILLA
Gorilla gorilla

The Gorilla is the largest primate: the male may be up to 180 cm tall and weigh as much as 275 kg, though the female is smaller. Gorillas are found in the rainforests of Equatorial West Africa, usually living in family groups of 2—30 animals, led by huge

Potto

Gorilla

Chimpanzee

CHIMPANZEE
Pan troglodytes

The Chimpanzee is the commonest of the primates. It is widespread in West and Central Equatorial Africa, living mainly in rainforests, but also in woodland savannahs and dry forests. Males weigh up to 100 kg, and females about 40 kg. Chimpanzees live in family groups of 2—50 members. They move adroitly over both ground and trees, usually running on all fours on the ground, but sometimes walking upright. They look for food in the daytime, and eat shoots, leaves and bark, pick fruit from trees and gather it up from the ground. Insects, birds' eggs and nestlings also form a major part of their diet, and they sometimes stalk and kill young baboons or antelopes for food.

After birth the single young clings to its mother's body for 5 months. Young Chimpanzees begin to walk when they are 6 months old, but they are looked after by their mothers until they become independent at the age of 4 years.

MANTLED GUEREZA
Colobus guereza

The Mantled Guereza is found in the forest regions of tropical Africa. This monkey, which weighs 13—23 kg, is notable for its 85-cm-long tail, covered in thick hair, which acts as a rudder to steer the animal through the air as it leaps from branch to branch. The Mantled Guereza lives in small troops in the crowns of tall trees. It eats mainly leaves, various fruits and seeds, and occasionally also catches insects. Troops of guerezas spend the night in habitual sleeping places in the midst of thick branches.

After a 6-month gestation period the female gives birth to a young monkey, which

males. They set out in the morning to search for food in their wide territories, picking fruit, berries, shoots and bark during their slow passage. Around noon they rest. For each night's sleep they build a special nest made of branches and leaves, and adult males sleep on the ground, females and young animals in trees.

When a young gorilla is born it clings firmly to its mother's stomach, not leaving her for 10 weeks. The offspring is suckled for a year and a half, and is looked after by its mother for the first four years of its life.

When gorillas are approached by humans, they try to frighten them off by beating on their chests with their hands. Gorillas do not usually attack humans, though a wounded animal may sometimes charge.

Mantled Guereza

Mandrill

is white all over. Three months later these offspring take on adult coloration.

MANDRILL
Mandrillus sphinx

The Mandrill is an inhabitant of the rain-forests of West Africa. It is a heavily-built monkey, the males weighing up to 54 kg, though females are much smaller. These members of the baboon family live mainly on the ground, either among shrubs or on dry rocky sites, but they usually sleep in the treetops. Mandrills feed on seeds, various fruits, roots, shoots, insects and small verte-brates. They sometimes enter plantations, where they cause considerable damage. An interesting feature of these monkeys is that they can swim well, and have no fear of water.
Young are born singly, or occasionally in pairs. The mothers carry their infants on

their chests, then when they are a little older they carry them on their backs.

DRILL
Mandrillus leucophaeus

The Drill is a powerful monkey, weighing 40 kg or more, which is found throughout the rainforests of West Africa, living in fam-ily groups under the leadership of the strongest male. The troop sets out in the morning to find food, picking various fruits or gathering them from the ground; they peel off bark, bite off shoots and blossoms, and catch insects and small vertebrates. Drills usually have a single offspring, which clings to its mother's stomach. Later, when the troop moves off to a new place, the young rides on its mother's back.
The females are mature at 3—4 years, the males at 5—6 years. Their enemies include leopards and large raptors.

De Brazza's Monkey

Drill

DE BRAZZA'S MONKEY
Cercopithecus neglectus

De Brazza's Monkey inhabits humid forests, especially along the banks of rivers in West and Equatorial Central Africa. Its body is 40—60 cm long, and its tail is up to a third longer. This finely-coloured monkey lives in troops of 15—20 members, but groups of up to 200 have been observed. In the early morning they set out in search of food, moving among the branches of trees and treetops, eating shoots, leaves, blossoms, fruit and seeds. Sometimes they will also eat ants or suck birds' eggs. In the evening these monkeys return to their usual overnight base in trees with thick foliage. Females give birth to one or sometimes two young.

RIVER HOG
Potamochoerus porcus

Rainforests, mountain woodland and thick scrubland savannahs are the habitat of the River Hog. It reaches a height of 60—75 cm, and weighs 55—80 kg. These hogs are gregarious, usually being found in small herds of 6—20 animals, led by the strongest male. During the day they take cover in thickets, foraging over their broad territory after dark. They often swim across small lakes or rivers during these nocturnal trips. River Hogs are omnivorous, devouring almost everything they come across. They eat fallen fruit, dig out roots, graze, catch insects and molluscs, prey on small vertebrates and also scavenge carrion. They often wander to plantations, damaging maize, millet or other crops.
Hidden in a thicket, the female gives birth to 3—6 young.

River Hog

Okapi

Greater Kudu

OKAPI
Okapia johnstoni

The Okapi inhabits the dense Ituri rainforests in Zaire. It is a large, giraffe-like mammal, reaching a height of 160 cm at the shoulders and weighing around 225 kg. Okapis live a solitary life, pairing only for a short while in the mating season. They spend the day in the shelter of thick vegetation, going out to feed only at night. Okapis eat leaves, twigs and the fruits of trees and bushes. They have excellent eyesight and hearing, and at the slightest sign of approaching danger these shy animals run off into the depths of the jungle, allowing few people to catch sight of them.
A single young weighing about 20 kg is born.

GREATER KUDU
Tragelaphus strepsiceros

The Greater Kudu is found in the open woodlands of eastern and southern Africa, both in flat countryside and in mountains, and in the rainy season it also comes out onto the savannahs. This huge antelope stands 160 cm tall at the shoulders and weighs 270—315 kg. Males have spiral horns up to 100 cm long, while females are hornless.

The Greater Kudu lives in small groups. During the day the animals rest in the shade of thickets, setting out to graze in the late afternoon. They feed on shoots and leaves of trees and bushes until morning, and eat fresh grass when it is available in the rainy season. This antelope is rare and lives under protection in national parks.
The female gives birth to a single calf among thick shrubs; this follows its mother and the herd on the second or third day.

BIRDS

CROWNED EAGLE
Stephanoaetus coronatus

The home of the Crowned Eagle is the forests, bushy savannahs and rocky tracts of Africa south of the Sahara. The wingspan of this stately bird of prey is 170 cm, and it weighs up to 3.8 kg. Crowned Eagles usually live in pairs, defending their hunting territory throughout the year. They usually hunt on the outskirts of forests or along wooded river banks, seeking their prey on the wing, flying rapidly but almost silently so their approach goes unnoticed. They snatch baby monkeys and hyraxes from trees, catch snakes from time to time, and have also been known to take a goat-kid from villages. A pair of Crowned Eagles builds a large nest of branches in a tall tree, 12—50 m above the ground. They use this for several successive years, adding to the nest each year, and lining it with small green twigs. The female lays 1 or 2 eggs, incubating them mainly on her own, though her mate may take over for a short time. He usually brings the mother bird her food until the young hatch; after that both parents feed the chicks. For the first two months the female prepares portions of food for them, then at the age of 103—115 days the young eagles are able to fly.

Crowned Eagle

Dark Chanting Goshawk

Long-tailed Hawk

DARK CHANTING GOSHAWK
Melierax metabates

The Dark Chanting Goshawk is distributed in West and Central Africa, extending to the south-western part of Saudi Arabia and to Tanzania in the south. Rainforests are its chief habitat. The male reaches a length of 45 cm and a wingspan of 90 cm, while the female measures about 55 cm and her wingspan is about 120 cm. In the nesting season the male perches on top of a tall tree and produces a melodious whistle, announcing the occupation of the territory. The partners build a relatively small nest in a tree, usually 10 m above the ground. The female lays

1—2 bluish eggs within several days and incubates the clutch for 33 days.

LONG-TAILED HAWK
Urotriorchis macrourus

The Long-tailed Hawk resides in the rainforests of West and Central Africa. Its total length is about 60 cm, including the tail, which is usually over 30 cm long. The wingspan is around 90 cm. The prey of this hawk consists of tree squirrels and small birds. It will also fly to the outskirts of villages situated near forests and take chickens. It kills its prey by crushing the neck with its formidable claws.

The nesting period is in July and August. A pair builds a nest of branches in a tall tree, some 20 m above the ground. Little is known of its nesting habits and of the rearing of the young.

CONGO SERPENT EAGLE
Dryotriorchis spectabilis

The Congo Serpent Eagle occurs in the forests of West and Equatorial Africa. It frequents thick treetops and has large eyes, adapted to permanent darkness. The wing-

Congo Serpent Eagle

span in both sexes is about 95 cm. It is a solitary bird, forming pairs only in the nesting season. It flies expertly and rapidly through the branches, rarely moving in open country.

The nesting period is from June to November. A pair builds a nest in the top of a tall tree. The structure is woven from twigs and is about 70 cm in diameter. Very little has been found out about the nesting habits of this interesting bird of prey.

Congo Peacock

CONGO PEACOCK
Afropavo congensis

The Congo Peacock inhabits rainforests in the Tschuapa River basin in Zaire. It settles in dense woodland at an altitude of 400 —1 800 m. The peacock measures up to 70 cm. The peahen is smaller and differs in colouring; the head crest, neck, underparts and tail being russet-tinged. Despite its noticeable size, it was discovered as late as 1936. It lives a sheltered life in remote and inaccessible places. It is one of rarest birds, seen only in a few zoological gardens, although young peafowl were recently successfully reared in captivity.

BRUCE'S GREEN PIGEON
Treron waalia

Bruce's Green Pigeon lives in thinly forested areas in the central part of the continent north of the equator, and it also occurs in south-western Arabia. It is about 30 cm long and both sexes are alike in colour.

In the nesting season, the pigeons stay in pairs, and afterwards the families unite to form flocks and fly among the tops of trees in search of food. They are difficult to observe because they are very quiet, and their colour makes them inconspicuous. They feed on various soft fruits, mainly figs. At night, they roost in the treetops, out of sight of their enemies.

BROWN-NECKED PARROT
Poicephalus robustus

The Brown-necked Parrot occurs in three subspecies in South and Central Africa, from which it extends to a part of the West African coast. It reaches 33 cm in length and has a typical massive bill. It is one of

Bruce's Green Pigeon

Brown-necked Parrot

Jardine's Parrot

the more plentiful birds in some regions, particularly in South Africa. It frequents dense forests up to a height of 1 250 m. In the Cape, it lives in forests with trees of the genus *Podocarpus*. Outside the nesting season, it flies in small flocks made up of pairs. The Brown-necked Parrot builds a nest in a tree hollow, usually some 6 m above the ground. The female lays 2—4 white eggs and incubates them for 26 days, while the male feeds her. The nestlings are fed by both parents for 9—11 weeks.

Meyer's Parrot

JARDINE'S PARROT
Poicephalus gulielmi

Jardine's Parrot is confined to the rainforests of Central and West Africa, and parts of East Africa. It measures about 28 cm and occurs in 4 subspecies. This parrot lives in mountains at a height of 3 500 m, but it does not ascend above this line. It is very common, particularly in forests where trees of the genera *Podocarpus* and *Cedrus* predominate, because it is fond of their fruits.
In the nesting season, each pair occupies its own individual territory. The nest is built in the hollow of a large tree, where the female lays 2—4 white eggs. She sits on them for 27 days, and the young are fed by both parents. The fledglings leave the nest when they are 10 weeks old.

MEYER'S PARROT
Poicephalus meyeri

Meyer's Parrot lives in Central and East Africa, part of its range extending to South

Rose-ringed Parakeet

Lilian's Lovebird

Red-headed Lovebird

Africa. It frequents forests and wooded savannahs containing huge baobabs of the genus *Adansonia*. It also settles along the banks of rivers, and in mountain forests up to 1 230 m. Meyer's Parrot feeds on various seeds and fruits. It nests in cavities, often in abandoned nests of woodpeckers or barbets, usually between July and December. The female lays 2—4 eggs on the lined bottom of the cavity. She sits on the clutch for 30 days, and the newly hatched young are fed by both parents.

RED-HEADED LOVEBIRD
Agapornis pullaria

The Red-headed Lovebird occurs in two subspecies, inhabiting sparse woodland and wooded savannahs in the central part of the African continent. This lovebird usually frequents the lowlands, although it may be found up to 1 400 m in montane areas. It is often seen near human settlements.

In the mating season lovebirds form pairs. They build nests in tree hollows or in termite mounds, in which they excavate tunnels and nesting holes. Most of the work is done by the female, and the male merely accompanies her.

LILIAN'S LOVEBIRD
Agapornis lilianae

Lilian's Lovebird lives in southern Tanzania, Malawi and Zambia, and is occasionally found in northern Zimbabwe. It measures 10—23.5 cm, being the smallest member of the genus *Agapornia*. The sexes are similar in appearance and difficult to distinguish.
In the breeding season, the pairs make nests in holes in trees, often near to each other. The female constructs a spherical nest from long stalks and bark strips, carrying the material in her beak, while the male accompanies her without offering any assistance. A clutch of about 8 eggs is incubated.

African Grey Parrot

The nest is built in tree hollows, usually from August to November. Parakeets prefer to use vacated woodpeckers' or barbets' nests. The female incubates 2—6 white eggs. She is only briefly relieved at the nest by the male. Incubation lasts 22—24 days, and both adults feed the young, who leave their nest at 6—7 weeks.

AFRICAN GREY PARROT
Psittacus erithacus

The African Grey Parrot is found from the west coast of Africa to Kenya and North-west Tanzania in lowland forests and wooded savannahs. Outside the mating season the birds go about in flocks of up to 100, and seek their food mainly in the tree-tops, chiefly eating seeds and different fruits. Sometimes they fly on to plantations in search of fruit, or visit suburban gardens and parks.

During the mating season these parrots live in pairs. They seek out a nesting site in the hollow of a huge tree 30 m above the ground. Here the female lays 2—4 eggs, which she incubates herself, though both parents then feed the young birds. These fly from the nest at the age of about 70 days.

ROSE-RINGED PARAKEET
Psittacula krameri

The Rose-ringed Parakeet is distributed as two subspecies in Africa and as two other subspecies in Asia. In Africa, it resides in forest areas of the central part of the continent. It reaches 40 cm in length and the female is easily distinguished from the male.

REPTILES

BLACK-NECKED SPITTING COBRA
Naja nigricollis

The Black-necked Spitting Cobra is found from West Africa to southern Egypt in the north and to the Transvaal in the south, and grows up to 2 m long. It is one of the so-

Black-necked Spitting Cobra

called spitting cobras, though in fact they spray their venom directly from fangs up to a distance of 4 m, aiming for their adversary's eyes. This may blind larger animals; with smaller ones, the venom absorbed through the mucous membrane of the eyes may kill them. Black-necked Spitting Cobras hide in holes throughout the day, hunting only at night. Their main diet is small rodents.

The female snake lays about 20 eggs in a hole in the ground, taking turns with the male to guard them, until the young are born 2 months later.

INVERTEBRATES

GOLIATH BEETLE
Goliathus regius

The giant Goliath Beetle lives in the forest regions of West Africa. It is most abundant in Cameroon. Its body may be more than 10 cm long, the female being smaller than the male. The female lays her eggs in rotting tree trunks, then the 20-cm-long larvae usually take 3 years to develop, before pupating in a small chamber made of saliva and decayed material. Emerging adult beetles fly into the treetops, where they eat parts of flowers and drink sap which oozes out of damaged branches or trunks.

This species is plentiful in some localities, and swarms of these beetles are a danger to road users, since they are capable of breaking windscreens.

Golden Hamster

Photograph by Jan Jeník

Ugandan Nile

RIVERS,
LAKES
AND
SWAMPS

MAMMALS

HIPPOPOTAMUS
Hippopotamus amphibius

The Hippopotamus lives in the rivers and lakes of West, Central and East Africa. It is 140—160 cm tall at the shoulders and may weigh up to 3 tonnes. Hippopotamuses are gregarious, forming herds of 10—30 animals. They are good swimmers and divers, submerging for up to 6 minutes at a time. During the day they rest in the water, with only their eyes and tightly closed nostrils above the surface, or they bask in the sun on some small island. After nightfall Hippopotamuses leave the water, and, using well-trodden paths, graze on the river banks. In a single night a Hippopotamus consumes about 60 kg of grass, water plants and different fruits. At the mating season males often fight each other savagely, inflicting severe wounds on their rivals with their teeth. Females give birth to a single calf, occasionally to twins, usually in the water. The calf weighs about 45 kg at birth, and is very active, taking its first breath and swimming off immediately.

PYGMY HIPPOPOTAMUS
Choeropsis liberiensis

The Pygmy Hippopotamus is found only in a small area of Liberia and the neighbouring part of Sierra Leone, though it has been observed in Guinea. It inhabits thick forests and bushland near rivers and swamps. This animal is 75 cm tall at the shoulders and weighs 160—270 kg. During the day it hides in damp places under eroded banks or lies in shallow water, then after dark it pushes its way through the thick vegetation along its usual tracks, and

Hippopotamus

Pygmy Hippopotamus

Defassa Waterbuck

Situtunga

feeds on leaves, fallen fruit, grass and green shoots.

This hippopotamus is a solitary creature, pairing only for a few days in the mating season. A single calf is born in a thicket, and its mother looks after it carefully.

SITUTUNGA
Tragelaphus spekei

The Situtunga is found from West Africa to Uganda and Zambia. It grows to a height of 115 cm at the shoulders, and weighs 45—110 kg. The male has horns up to 90 cm long, but the female has no horns and is smaller. The Situtunga has long hooves, which allow it to move rapidly across marshy ground or among growths of reeds or papyrus. During the day this antelope is often found in water, and it can swim well. After dark it searches for food, eating leaves, twigs, grass, water plants and

fallen fruit. The Situtunga lives in small herds of 10—15 animals, the leader of which is a strong, highly-coloured male. In a dry spot on an island the female gives birth to one or occasionally two young. These are spotted, which helps them to hide from predators amid dense vegetation.

DEFASSA WATERBUCK
Kobus defassa

One of the largest antelopes is the Defassa Waterbuck: it reaches a height of 120—135 cm at the shoulder and weighs 160—270 kg. Males have horns up to 1 m long, while females have none. Defassa Waterbuck are to be found near rivers and lakes, where there is plenty of grass and other plants throughout the year, and they seek shelter in dense reed beds. They go out to graze in the morning and evening, and often visit water-holes, drinking large

71

amounts of water. They live in small herds of 5—30, led by a strong male.

Under cover of a thicket, the female gives birth to a single young, which is suckled for 6—7 months, though young Defassa Waterbuck are able to fend for themselves at the age of 3 months if necessary. Their chief enemies are lions and leopards.

BIRDS

LESSER FLAMINGO
Phoeniconaias minor

The Lesser Flamingo is found mainly in the salty lakes of West, East and South Africa, and is the most common of all flamingoes — there are over three million of them in Africa, and colonies sometimes number several hundred thousand birds. A female flamingo makes herself a conical nest about 30 cm high from mud, sand and decaying plant material on a river bank or in shallow water. She then usually lays a single egg, which she mostly incubates herself. For three weeks both parents feed the young chick with a special paste, formed during this period in the stomachs of the parents. Parents can recognize their own young among the flocks of birds by their voices. Adult flamingoes feed on small crustaceans, molluscs, worms, insect larvae and plant particles. Their food is sieved through a system of long grooves along the sides of their beaks.

MARABOU STORK
Leptoptilus crumeniferus

The Marabou Stork is a large bird, about 150 cm tall and weighing up to 7 kg. It is

Marabou Stork

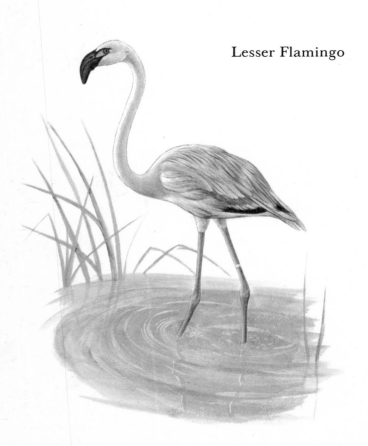
Lesser Flamingo

native to almost the whole of Africa, being found mainly along the banks of rivers and lakes, but also in the savannahs. It hunts frogs, small mammals and reptiles, catches locusts and other large insects in the savannahs, and frequently feeds on carrion and animal remains. It often flies into towns, where it seeks out rubbish tips and eats anything that is remotely edible.

In the nesting season marabou live in colonies. Individual pairs make themselves large nests of branches and twigs, usually in tall, isolated trees. The female lays 3 eggs, which both parents take turns to incubate. They feed the young birds by disgorging food directly into the nest.

SHOEBILL or WHALE-HEADED STORK
Balaeniceps rex

The Shoebill, or Whale-headed Stork, is a powerfully built wader, standing up to 150 cm tall, and inhabiting the swamps of the Sudan, Zaire and Uganda. It can be found in river basins, among extensive growths of papyrus and reeds. Outside the nesting season these birds are solitary, only pairing in order to nest. They build themselves large nests of sticks, reeds and water plants among the reed beds in the middle of broad expanses of marsh. The female lays 2 blue-grey eggs, taking turns with her mate to incubate them, and both parents then feed the young on small fish. Fish is the chief food of the adult birds, as well as frogs and insects. The birds greet their mates by snapping their curiously-shaped bills.

HAMMERHEAD
Scopus umbretta

The Hammerhead, a 60-cm-tall wader, is found from Sierra Leone eastwards to Somalia, and southwards through the whole of Africa, as well as Morocco and Madagascar. It lives on the tree- and bush-covered banks of lakes and slow-moving rivers, or on the edges of forests near water. During the day these birds sit under cover of dense branches, setting off after dark to hunt in-

Hammerhead

Shoebill or Whale-headed Stork

Sacred Ibis

African Fish Eagle

sects, crustaceans, molluscs, fish and frogs. Outside the breeding season they form small colonies, but they nest in pairs, each pair defending its own territory. They build themselves an enormous roofed nest, completely closed and measuring up to 2.5 m in diameter, in a tree. It is made of twigs, reeds, leaves, pieces of wood and even the bones of dead animals. The entrance to the nest leads obliquely upwards from below. The Hammerheads squeeze adroitly through the small opening, but no enemy can get inside. The female lays 4—6 eggs, which are incubated by both parents. Young Hammerheads can fly after 7—8 weeks.

SACRED IBIS
Threskiornis aethiopicus

The Sacred Ibis is a wader, about 75 cm tall, which is common in swampy regions and on the banks of large rivers and lakes throughout almost the whole of Africa. In some areas these birds are resident; in others they come visiting in large flocks at times of floods. The Sacred Ibis hunts fish, reptiles, molluscs, worms and insects. In ancient Egypt these birds were thought to bring a good harvest, for which reason they were considered sacred, but the ibises actually visited Egypt in flood years because of the rich prey they found in the shallows and pools.

The Sacred Ibis lives in colonies, even at the nesting season, and several hundred birds may be found together. Individual pairs usually build their nests of twigs, lined with soft grass, in treetops. The female lays 2—3 bluish-white eggs, which the parents take turns to sit on, and they both feed the young by regurgitation. Young ibises are able to fly at the age of 8 weeks.

AFRICAN FISH EAGLE
Haliaeetus vocifer

The areas around Africa's rivers, lakes and the coast are the home of the African Fish Eagle. This splendid bird of prey has a wingspan of about 2.3 m and weighs

3.5 kg. Outside the mating season these eagles often hunt in groups of up to 60 birds. Their main prey is fish, though they sometimes take the young of flamingoes and herons.

During the nesting season individual pairs defend their own territories, at which time the clear call of the male can often be heard. The eagles usually build their nest at the top of a tree, and make it out of branches lined with pieces of papyrus or reeds. The female lays 1—3 eggs, mostly sitting on them herself, though she is sometimes relieved by her mate. The young eagles begin to fly at the age of 65—75 days.

ROYAL CRANE
Balearica regulorum

Damp and grassy places near lakes and large rivers from Zaire and Uganda southwards to the Cape are inhabited by the Royal Crane. Outside the nesting season they can be found in flocks by the waterside, but when nesting they live in pairs. They seek out swampy places with shallow pools, and under cover of the reeds or on an overgrown island they build a large nest from sticks and reeds. The female lays 2—3 pale blue eggs, and both parents take turns to incubate the clutch. The young hatch after 29—31 days, and are able to leave the nest soon afterwards. During the first few days their parents put food in their beaks. The Royal Crane lives on insects, small vertebrates, green shoots, berries and seeds.

ALLEN'S GALLINULE
Porphyrula alleni

Allen's Gallinule is found throughout Africa south of the Sahara, in lakes and creeks thickly overgrown with vegetation. It often walks across the leaves of water plants in

Allen's Gallinule

Royal Crane

search of food, and eats seeds, the green parts of plants and flowers, as well as catching insects and other invertebrates. It builds its nest of plant materials in the reeds or swamps. The female lays 2—5 eggs, which she and her mate take turns to incubate. During the first few days the parent birds bring food for the chicks in their beaks, but the young are soon able to look after themselves.

AFRICAN JACANA or LILY-TROTTER
Actophilornis africanus

The African Jacana, or Lily-trotter, which is conspicuous for its very long toes, is found in the whole of Africa south of the Sahara. It lives in creeks and on lakes and swampy pools, running skilfully over the large leaves of water plants in search of food. Jacanas eat insects, molluscs, spiders, seeds and parts of plants. They usually live in pairs, the two birds working together to build a nest in the reeds out of long-leaved plants. The female lays 2—5 eggs, decorated with black and dark-brown streaks and spots, which are then incubated by the male, who also looks after the young on his own, bringing them food in his beak during the first few days of their life.

PIED KINGFISHER
Ceryle rudis

The Pied Kingfisher inhabits rivers, lakes and irrigation channels throughout almost the whole of Africa. It is 23 cm long and both male and female have the same colouring. Kingfishers frequently fly slowly over the water, sometimes hovering over one spot so as to see their prey better. They catch their food by diving into the water with folded wings, and eat small fish, crustaceans and insects.

Nesting birds dig a burrow in a sandy or clayey bank. The burrow consists of

African Jacana or Lily-trotter

Pied Kingfisher

a 1-m-long passage leading to a spacious nesting chamber. From 4—6 eggs are laid, and the female usually incubates them alone. Both parents feed the young, which leave the nest after 25 days, then learn to hunt for a further 14 days.

REPTILES

NILE CROCODILE
Crocodylus niloticus

Nile Crocodiles live in quite large numbers in some African river basins and lakes, and in Madagascar. These reptiles grow to a length of 5 m and a weight of more than a tonne. They are extremely agile in the water, where they hunt their prey, mainly fish, crabs and other reptiles. Large crocodiles also attack antelopes and other large animals at watering places, though young crocodiles live on insects, spiders and small fish. Females dig a hole by the waterside in which to lay 30—50 eggs, which have a hard shell. The mother covers the eggs with sand, then stays close to the nest, guarding the eggs until they begin to hatch. After 8—9 weeks the fully-developed young crocodiles begin to call. When the mother hears them, she scrapes away the sand and helps her offspring out, but does not care for them after that.

Nile Crocodile

AMPHIBIANS

AFRICAN CLAWED TOAD
Xenopus laevis

The African Clawed Toad is found in the waters of South Africa, in places with a muddy bed. Here this toad searches for food, eating worms, molluscs and insect larvae. When the waters dry up, it buries itself in the mud and sleeps through the dry season. Soon after the rains come the female lays her eggs in a tangle of water plants, and two days later larvae hatch out.

African Clawed Toad

FISH

LUNGFISH
Protopterus dolloi

The Lungfish *Protopterus dolloi* lives in stagnant or sluggish waters of the Congo River basin. It has a slender, eel-like body about 1 m long, entirely covered in tiny scales, and its paired limbs look more like legs than fins, although they are not able to support the creature. Its coloration is variable. It uses its gills to take in oxygen from the water, but it is able to come to the surface and breathe in air, using its lung-like air bladder. It feeds on small fishes and frogs, and young individuals eat worms, insects and larvae.

BICHIR
Polypterus bichir

The Bichir *Polypterus bichir* is confined to the Upper Nile and to lakes Rudolf and Chad, but some may be carried by the stream and get as far as Cairo. This fish is about 1 m long, and its body structure is very primitive. The body is covered with rhomboidal scales and the dorsal fin is divided into a series of finlets with bony protuberances in front. Bichirs have a bilobed air bladder which is connected to the digestive tract. They come to the surface for air.

Nine other species of this family live in rivers and lakes of tropical Africa.

BUTTERFLY FISH
Pantodon buchholzi

The Butterfly Fish, which grows to a length of 10—12 cm, inhabits tropical waters of West Africa in the area from Nigeria to Zaire, being most abundant in the basins of the rivers Niger and Congo. This fish gets such a name because its long, wing-like pectoral fins are reminiscent of a butterfly.

MORMYRID
Gnathonemus petersi

The Mormyrid *Gnathonemus petersi* inhabits

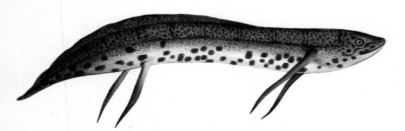

Lungfish *Protopterus dolloi*

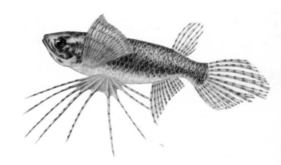

Butterfly Fish

Bichir *Polypterus bichir*

Mormyrid *Gnathonemus petersi*

Killifish *Epiplatys annulatus*

Jewel Fish or Red Cichlid

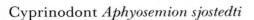

Cyprinodont *Aphyosemion sjostedti*

Mozambique Mouthbrooder

the rivers of West Africa from the Niger River basin to the Congo watershed. It is about 23 cm long and is characterized by an extremely elongated and mobile lower lip with cells sensitive to mechanical and chemical stimuli.

KILLIFISH
Epiplatys annulatus

The Killifish *Epiplatys annulatus* is a beautifully coloured fish only 3 — 4 cm long. It inhabits waters from Guinea to Liberia, frequenting shallow sites overgrown with vegetation. The female is smaller than the male and her tail and fins are usually uniformly yellow. There are several colour varieties.

This fish feeds on tiny crustaceans and small larvae, mainly those of gnats, collected at the surface.

JEWEL FISH or RED CICHLID
Hemichromis bimaculatus

The Jewel Fish, or Red Cichlid, which reaches a length of about 15 cm, occurs in the Niger, Nile and Congo rivers and in

their tributaries. It is extremely common. It is magnificently coloured in the breeding season, the male being red with emerald spots, and the female having a yellow front half, while the hind part of her body is red. Spawning takes place on the bottom.

CYPRINODONT
Aphyosemion sjostedti

The Cyprinodont *Aphyosemion sjostedti* is distributed in southern Nigeria and western Cameroon. It lives in slow or stagnant water. Spawning of this species takes place in fine sand on the bottom. The female buries her eggs in the sand and they hatch in 3 — 9 weeks. After 2 — 3 days, the young begin swimming around and catching gnat larvae and small crustaceans.

MOZAMBIQUE MOUTHBROODER
Tilapia mossambica

The Mozambique Mouthbrooder is widespread in fresh and brackish waters of East Africa, ranging to the southern parts of the continent. It is about 35 cm long.

In the breeding season the male occupies

Red Lyretail

Cichlid *Labeotropheus fuelleborni*

Cichlid *Pseudotropheus zebra*

Cyprinodont *Aphyosemion gardneri*

a territory and defends it vigorously. The female lays 300—400 eggs in a shallow depression on the bottom, digging it with her mouth. When the male has discharged his milt, the female picks up the fertilized eggs and retains them in a special mouth pouch until the fry hatch out.

CYPRINODONT
Aphyosemion gardneri

The Cyprinodont *Aphyosemion gardneri* is native to the waters of tropical West Africa, mainly Nigeria and western Cameroon. It reaches 6 cm in length, and there are two colour varieties. Males of the first variety have rich yellow-edged fins and tails, and males of the second have greenish, red-spotted fins. Females of both varieties are drab, grey-green above and pale violet below.

RED LYRETAIL
Aphyosemion bivittatum

The Red Lyretail is found in West Africa, particularly in the Niger River estuary, and it extends to Togo. It lives in swamps with pools, often tiny ones, and in small lakes scattered throughout the steppe zone. It is

about 5 cm long and the coloration of the males is variable. In some individuals the dorsal, caudal and anal fins are elongated and flag-shaped, while in others they are branched.

CICHLID
Labeotropheus fuelleborni

The Cichlid *Labeotropheus fuelleborni* is native to Lake Malawi, formerly called Nyassa. frequenting its rocky shores. It measures about 14 cm. The males are blue, with dark transverse stripes. For the most part females are black, with orange-brown mottling, but forms with vertical stripes also exist. Some females are bluish and resemble the males. The female collects the fertilized eggs in her mouth and they hatch there. Afterwards she looks after the fry.
This cichlid feeds mainly on algae growing on rocks.

CICHLID
Pseudotropheus zebra

The Cichlid *Pseudotropheus zebra* is also indigenous to Lake Malawi, this lake being the home of many members of the genus *Pseudotropheus*. The cichlid is 15 cm long

Mudskipper *Periophthalmus koelreuteri*

Climbing Perch *Ctenopoma fasciolatum*

Sebae Silverfish

and some specimens are pale blue or bluish-white in colour. It inhabits rocky sites covered with thick layers of algae, and the males defend large territories.

The fish feeds on tiny invertebrates, algae and parts of water plants.

MUDSKIPPER
Periophthalmus koelreuteri

The Mudskipper *Periophthalmus koelreuteri* is distributed along the coasts of East Africa, Madagascar, southern Asia and Australia. Some zoologists distinguish several species. This interesting fish grows to 15 cm in length and has bulging, lidded eyes. Its habitats are on muddy shores or in river estuaries. Supported by their fins, which they use as legs, mudskippers crawl ashore, moving in jumps. They even climb on to branches which touch the surface of the water, promptly diving back if they are disturbed. They are able to remain on land for several hours at a time, their gills being protected from drying by special covers.

CLIMBING PERCH
Ctenopoma fasciolatum

The Climbing Perch *Ctenopoma fasciolatum*

is distributed in the Congo River basin in West Africa. It is about 8 cm long, and its characteristic feature is a markedly wide dorsal fin. It feeds on insects, larvae, worms, tiny crustaceans and small fishes, and it sometimes eats plant food.

The males become hostile in the breeding season, and defend their territories from intruders.

SEBAE SILVERFISH
Monodactylus sebae

The Sebae Silverfish is native to river estuaries, ranging from Senegal to Zaire. It lives near the shore, sometimes in brackish waters, and it may wander upstream into inland regions. It occurs in large shoals, mainly among mangrove roots, and it can swim very quickly. It is adapted for life among thick aquatic weeds.

Photograph by Bořivoj Záruba

North-western Libya, Hamada al Homra

MOUNTAINOUS
AND
ROCKY
AREAS

———

MAMMALS

GELADA BABOON
Theropithecus gelada

The Gelada Baboon has a body 75 cm long and a tail up to 80 cm long; it weighs about 20 kg. It lives in rocky and mountainous parts of Ethiopia, at a height of 1 800—4 000 m. This baboon forms troops led by a strong adult male. Each animal or family has its own home in a small cave, where it sleeps at night and hides when frightened. In the morning they go in search of food, feeding on grass, the fruit of bushes and trees, seeds and roots on the rocky slopes.
A single offspring is born, which is carried on its mother's stomach while young.

ROCK HYRAX or DASSIE
Procavia capensis

The Rock Hyrax, or Dassie, lives in rocky areas throughout the savannahs of South Africa. It grows to a length of 45—55 cm and weighs 2—4 kg. Rock Hyraxes are very gregarious, and usually live in colonies of about 50. During the day they eat grass and the leaves of low bushes, or feed on fallen fruit. While the group is eating, a number of older animals always keep watch. If danger threatens, the whole group runs off and the hyraxes are soon hidden away in their lairs in rock crevices. They go to drink only during very dry periods, when there is not enough juicy food available.
Females usually give birth to 1—2 young, and occasionally up to 6. These are sighted at birth, and within a few hours are very active, beginning to eat grass when they are 3 days old.

MOUNTAIN ZEBRA
Equus zebra

The Mountain Zebra is found in mountainous regions of South Africa, in the Cape Province. It stands 125 cm tall at the shoulders and weighs about 270 kg. Its habitat is dry, rocky places, though when food is scarce it moves into grassland semidesert areas in search of fresh grass. These zebras live in small groups, usually of 5—12 animals, led by an old, experienced mare. The animals eat grass, and visit water-holes once every three days.
The female gives birth to a single foal, which is left lying hidden in the bushes or

Gelada Baboon

Rock Hyrax or Dassie

84

Mountain Zebra

Barbary Sheep or Aoudad

long grass for 3—6 days, though its mother stays nearby and suckles it regularly. The young zebra then follows its mother and joins the herd.

AFRICAN WILD ASS
Equus africanus

Today the African Wild Ass is found only in northern Somalia and Ethiopia. It is a large hoofed mammal, reaching a height of 140 cm at the shoulders, and it lives in small herds of 10—15 animals. Their home is in desert areas of plateaux at a height of about 2 000 m. Here they graze on the sparse, tough grass, shoots and low, thorny bushes. They visit water-holes daily unless they have found particularly juicy food, in which case they drink every two or three days.
Females give birth to a single young, which they suckle for almost a year, though at the age of 3 months the foals begin to eat grass. However, they drink no water for the first half year.

BARBARY SHEEP or AOUDAD
Ammotragus lervia

The Barbary Sheep, or Aoudad, lives in rocky places in the mountainous regions of North Africa. It is more closely related to

the goat than to the sheep. The male, which has a huge mane and horns up to 90 cm long, reaches a height of 100 cm at the shoulders and a weight of over 120 kg. The female is much smaller, with thinner, shorter horns. The Barbary Sheep lives in family herds. During the day they rest in the shade of overhanging rocks, going to graze in the valleys only in the evening or at night. They eat grass, herbs, and the leaves and twigs of bushes and low trees.
Pregnant females leave the herd, giving birth to 1—3 young in an inaccessible spot. The lambs usually lie hidden for a few days among the rocks, and their mothers come to suckle them, though within a few hours of being born they are capable of following their mothers over the steep, rocky slopes.

African Wild Ass

BIRDS

VERREAUX'S EAGLE
Aquila verreauxi

Verreaux's Eagle is a robust bird of prey, weighing up to 3.7 kg, with a wingspan of 2 m. It lives in rocky and mountainous areas south of the Sahara as far as Zimbabwe, and east to Sudan, Ethiopia and Somalia. At the mating season the eagles fly to a great height, then soar and dive, gliding for hours above the valleys and ravines. A pair of birds builds a nest on a rocky ledge from branches, lined with fine twigs. The female lays 2—3 eggs, which she sits on all night; in the daytime her mate takes his turn. In the early days after the young have hatched the male brings food for both them and their mother; later both parents go hunting.

The main prey of these eagles is hyraxes, and they also catch guineafowl, young antelopes, mongooses and domestic poultry. The young are able to fly at the age of 95—100 days.

MASKED LOVEBIRD
Agapornis personata

The Masked Lovebird is about 14.5 cm long, and is found in the mountainous regions of North-east Tanzania and Kenya, at a height of 1 100—1 700 m. It is found on grassy plateaux, where there are numerous growths of acacia and occasional baobabs, and feeds on seeds, berries and fruit. The birds nest in the hollows of trees: the female crams thin twigs and strips of bark into the hollow, then makes a small nesting chamber with a short, tunnel-like side entrance. She lays 4—7 eggs; when

Verreaux's Eagle

Masked Lovebird

these hatch the young are fed by both parents. After 44 days the young lovebirds fly.

HERMIT IBIS or WALDRAPP
Geronticus eremita

The rare Hermit Ibis, or Waldrapp, inhabits the coastal cliffs of Morocco, but it will also settle on rocky ledges in the middle of towns. This wader stands 75 cm tall and weighs 1.35 kg. Hermit Ibises form colonies: individual pairs build their nests of small twigs, blades of grass, seaweed, pieces of turf and small pebbles, on rocky ledges. Nests in a colony are about 80 cm apart. The female lays 2—3 eggs, which both parents take turns to sit on. The young are fed on a paste of insects, regurgitated from their parents' crops, for the first 2 weeks, then the young begin to fly at the age of 7 weeks.

Hermit Ibis or Waldrapp

Adults mostly feed on beetles, mainly scarabs, locusts and mole crickets, but they sometimes hunt lizards, frogs and freshwater molluscs.

INVERTEBRATES

WEST AFRICAN SCORPION
Pandinus imperator

The West African Scorpion reaches a length of up to 20 cm and is the largest scorpion in the world. It is found in rocky areas in West Africa. During the day it hides in moist rock crevices or under large, flat stones, then in the evening it crawls out and goes in search of prey. It catches insects and worms in its huge claws, and sometimes also takes the young of small vertebrates. On the end of its tail it has a poisonous sting, but the venom is not particularly strong, and is not dangerous to man.

The female gives birth to live young, which climb up on their mother's back. There they feed on prey caught by the adult, fending for themselves after 3—4 weeks.

West African Scorpion

South-western Libya, the sea of sand at Ubari

DESERTS
AND
SEMIDESERTS

MAMMALS

ANUBIS BABOON
Papio anubis

The Anubis Baboon is a powerfully built ape. The male's body is 100 cm long, its tail is 70 cm long, and it weighs 22—50 kg. The female is only half his size. The Anubis Baboon is found in stony semidesert regions containing rock formations or in the dry, grassy areas from the southern Sahara to Uganda and Kenya. These apes always live near water, where they go to drink regularly every day. They live in troops of 12—300 animals, led by the strongest male. When they go in search of food the troop is well-organized: females with young walk in the middle, with strong, adult but subordinate males at the front and strong, adult males at the rear. Not even a leopard dare attack such a foraging party as this.

At night Anubis Baboons find themselves caves to sleep in. They feed on shoots, berries, fruit, bark and invertebrates, but the larger individuals will attack and kill young Thomson's Gazelles or domestic goats.

Females usually give birth to a single young, which the mother carries on her stomach until the infant is 2 months old, when it rides on her back.

FENNEC FOX
Fennecus zerda

The Fennec Fox is a small canine carnivore with unusually large ears. It is 20 cm tall at the shoulders, weighs about 1.5 kg, and is widespread in North African deserts. It digs a burrow 1.5 m deep in the sand, where it hides in the daytime, leaving its lair to go in search of food at night, when several animals will often hunt together. Fennec Foxes eat insects, scorpions, lizards, small rodents, birds, berries and birds' eggs. They can go for several days without water, but drink regularly at oases.

The female gives birth to 2—5 young in an underground lair lined with soft hair and leaves.

GRÉVY'S ZEBRA
Equus grevyi

Grévy's Zebra is the largest species of zebra, measuring 160 cm at the shoulders and weighing 350—450 kg. It is found in semi-

Anubis Baboon

Fennec Fox

Grévy's Zebra

Scimitar-horned Oryx

deserts and dry bushland in East Africa, living in small groups of 4—15 animals. It mainly grazes, but also browses on the leaves of bushes and low trees. It can go without water for several days, and usually visits water-holes once every two or three days.

The female has a single foal, which is active and stands up 15 minutes after birth.

SCIMITAR-HORNED ORYX
Oryx dammah

The Scimitar-horned Oryx is a heavily-built antelope which stands 120 cm tall at the shoulders and weighs over 200 kg. The male is stronger than the female, and has heavier and longer horns. This antelope is now found only along the southern edge of the Sahara, living in small herds of 10—15 animals led by the strongest of the males. These groups roam from place to place in search of grass, acacia leaves, succulents and various fruits to eat.

The female has one or occasionally two young.

BIRDS

AFRICAN LAPPET-FACED VULTURE
Torgos tracheliotus

The Lappet-faced Vulture is the largest of the African vultures, with a wingspan of up to 2.6 m. It is widespread in deserts, semi-deserts and open bushland from the Sahara eastwards to Somalia and southwards to the Cape. They are often found in groups, particularly around the carcasses of large mammals. They also kill smaller animals for food, and eat locusts, termites and the eggs of other birds.

African Lappet-faced Vulture

Lappet-faced Vultures build their nests from branches in the crown of an acacia tree or on the horizontal branch of a huge baobab. The nest is lined with grass, or with pieces of rag and camel hair. The female lays a single egg, which both parents take turns to incubate; both birds also feed the young, which leaves the nest after 110—120 days.

REPTILES

COMMON SKINK
Scincus scincus

The Common Skink, a lizard 20 cm long or more, inhabits the sandy deserts of North Africa. It can dig itself rapidly into soft ground, even travelling underneath the sand to escape from enemies. The Common Skink feeds on insects, spiders and small scorpions.

Common Skink

EGYPTIAN COBRA
Naja haje

The Egyptian Cobra is found in deserts, semideserts and bushy plains throughout almost the whole of Africa. It averages 2 m in length, and is one of the largest venomous snakes. During the day it hides in piles of stones, holes under shrubs or the burrows of mammals, going in search of prey after dark. Its main victims are rodents, in search of which it will often enter human habitations. A man may step on a cobra in the dark, when the cobra will bite him in self-defence. Its venom is highly dangerous, and can prove fatal unless serum is available.

Egyptian Cobra

Saw-scaled Viper

Tornier's Tortoise

Horned Viper

During the mating season cobras live in pairs. The female lays about 20 eggs in a hole dug in the sand with her mouth, then the parents guard the clutch in the entrance passage to the burrow. The young snakes are born after 2 months, and are immediately independent.

In Egypt this cobra is often used by fakirs in their performances.

SAW-SCALED VIPER
Echis carinatus

The Saw-scaled Viper is native to North and East Africa as far as Lake Turkana, but it is also found in south-western and southern Asia. It is about 60 cm long, and its ground coloration varies from tawny or buffish to pale red. It is most common in sandy deserts, but it is also found in clayey and stony sites. The female gives birth to 3—15 young and the new-born vipers are immediately independent.

HORNED VIPER
Cerastes cerastes

The Horned Viper inhabits sandy deserts of North Africa, mainly in the north-eastern area. It can be as long as 75 cm, but the average length is 50 cm. It is characterized by a short tail and two long, pointed scales above the eyes, resembling horns. The female bears 5—12 live young. They are independent from birth and immediately scatter over the neighbourhood. The venom of this viper is very effective.

TORNIER'S TORTOISE
Malacochersus tornieri

Tornier's Tortoise lives in the equatorial area of East Africa. This bizarre tortoise has a markedly flattened, pliable carapace 20—24 cm long, under which it cannot pull its head or feet. On the other hand, it can easily hide in narrow rock crevices. When alarmed, it runs with great speed, which is unusual in a land tortoise, and it tries to hide.

The female lays only 5 eggs. They are about 5 cm long, and have tough shells.

hundreds. Sometimes they are found in small pools at oases or beside irrigated fields. The females lay clusters of eggs in the water.

TOAD
Bufo mauretanicus

The Toad *Bufo mauretanicus* is about 12 cm long and inhabits semideserts and desert edges in Morocco and Tunisia. It frequents places with sandy soil covered in tufts of grass, plants and shrubs. Early in spring, these toad congregate near water, often in

Toad *Bufo mauretanicus*

INVERTEBRATES

SPIDER
Eresus niger

The Spider *Eresus niger* lives in deserts, semideserts and dry grassland of North Africa. It occurs in warmer regions of Europe and extends to Central Asia. The female is about 15 mm long, and the male about 12 mm. The female is velvety black, while the male is characterized by a red, black-dotted abdomen.

Spider *Eresus niger*

SCORPION
Buthus occitanus

The Scorpion *Buthus occitanus,* which is about 8 cm long, is distributed mainly in North Africa, but it also occurs in southern and south-eastern Europe. It inhabits the edges of desert regions and of semideserts. The scorpion's sting is not dangerous to

Scorpion *Buthus occitanus*

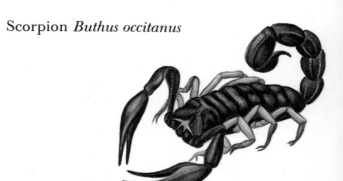

man, although it is painful and the wound swells up. The pain usually subsides after about 6 hours, depending on the sensitivity of the individual.

Mediterranean Stick Insect

MEDITERRANEAN STICK INSECT
Bacillus rossii

The Mediterranean Stick Insect is found in North Africa, and occasionally in southern Europe. It frequents bushes or low trees growing on the edges of deserts and in semideserts. The female measures as much as 10 cm, but the male is smaller. The insect feeds on the leaves of various shrubs. Its long body and green coloration give it the appearance of a twig, and when it holds its legs close against its body, it entirely escapes the attention of its enemies.

The female lays rounded eggs on leaves or expels them in the air, letting them drop to the ground. The eggs hatch into tiny larvae, similar in their bodily make-up to adult Stick Insects.

Sacred Scarab

SACRED SCARAB
Scarabaeus sacer

The Sacred Scarab beetle, which is 3 cm long, lives in the deserts and semideserts of North Africa. It is common in places inhabited by camels, goats, sheep or large wild mammals, since it feeds on their droppings. From these it moulds a ball of dung for food, which is often much bigger than the beetle itself. The female makes a dung-ball for its offspring, burying this in an underground chamber. Here it shapes the food store into the form of a pear and lays an egg on its point, so the larva has a ready-made larder. When it has eaten all the food and finished growing, it pupates, and in a few weeks a new beetle hatches out.

In Ancient Egypt the Scarab Beetle was considered sacred, and was a symbol of rebirth. The Ancient Egyptians believed that Scarabs crawling to the surface were 'born of earth and sand' and that they could bring about the reincarnation of the dead. The Sacred Scarab was one of the emblems of the pharaohs.

Photograph by Jan Jeník

South-western Madagascar, near Tongobora

MADAGASCAR

MAMMALS

COMMON TENREC
Tenrec ecaudatus

The Common Tenrec is a strange-looking, 30- to 40-cm-long insectivore. It is a native of Madagascar, where it lives in bushy areas or sparse forests. Throughout the day it lies hidden in an underground burrow which it digs for itself, setting out in search of food after dark. It creeps along the banks of streams and pools or among damp, fallen leaves, mainly seeking worms, molluscs and insect larvae, and it sometimes eats sweet fallen fruit.

The female gives birth to a litter of 12—30 young at a time in her burrow. These open their eyes after 10 days, and are suckled for one month.

RING-TAILED LEMUR
Lemur catta

The tropical mountain rainforests of Madagascar are the home of the Ring-tailed Lemur. This is a primate about 40 cm long, with a tail 50 cm long. Ring-tailed Lemurs are diurnal animals—they are active during the day. They usually keep to the treetops, leaping nimbly from branch to branch. Their bushy tails act as a rudder, helping them to steer. These lemurs feed on insects, geckos, tree frogs and young birds. They like to suck birds' eggs, and are fond of sweet, juicy fruit or berries. They drink by dipping their forepaws in the water and then licking them.

Ring-tailed Lemurs live in families or small troops. In a spacious tree hollow the female gives birth to one or rarely two young. At first the offspring clings to its mother's stomach, later riding on her back.

Ring-tailed Lemur   Common Tenrec

Mongoose Lemur

MONGOOSE LEMUR
Lemur mongos

The Mongoose Lemur lives in the mountain forests of North-west Madagascar and in the Comoro Islands. The male is distinguished by his red cheeks, the female's being white. During the day these lemurs shelter in the hollows of trees, rolled up in a ball and sleeping soundly. After sunset they crawl around the treetops in search of insects, larvae, birds' eggs and sweet fruit. The female gives birth to a single young, which she carries on her stomach. After 5 weeks the young lemur climbs among the branches itself, though it is carefully supervised by its mother.

RUFFED LEMUR
Varecia variegatus

The rare Ruffed Lemur lives in trees in the forests of Madagascar. Its body is about

Ruffed Lemur

60 cm long, and its bushy tail about the same length. In the daytime it sleeps in the hollows of trees or the disused nests of birds of prey. After sunset it wakes up and sets off to look for food, searching for soft fruit, insects, small vertebrates and birds' eggs.
The female gives birth to twins or triplets, usually in the hollow of a tree trunk. The mother leaves the young in this lair, but comes regularly to suckle them.

INDRI
Indri indri

The Indri is found in the mountainous rain-forests on the east coast of Madagascar. It is

Indri

Aye-aye

a 65-cm-long primate with a short tail, which lives in the thick crowns of trees or tall bushes. Indris live in families or small troops which wander about among the treetops during the day in search of fruit, berries and birds' eggs. They also hunt insects and young geckos, and like to eat birds. Their skill at birdcatching used to be exploited by native hunters who trained young Indris to hunt for them and carry back the prey.

The female gives birth to a single young, which she carries with her everywhere.

AYE-AYE
Daubentonia madagascariensis

The Aye-aye is a curious primate from Madagascar. It is 36—44 cm long, and its tail measures 50—60 cm. It lives in extensive bamboo thickets, and uses its strong incisors to bite open the bamboo stalks, looking for hidden insects and their larvae. It

then uses the thin, curved claw of its long middle finger to extract its victim. It also eats birds' eggs, various fruits and bamboo shoots, seeking its food only at night; in the daytime it remains hidden in the hollows of thick branches.

Aye-ayes live alone or in pairs. The female builds a round nest of leaves among the bamboo thickets, which has an entrance at the side. She gives birth to a single young.

FOSSA
Cryptoprocta ferox

The Fossa is the largest of the Madagascar carnivores. Its long, slender body is 90 cm long, and its tail is the same length. The Fossa is found in forests, where it shelters during the day in large hollows in trees or the forks of thick branches. At night it creeps among the treetops in search of birds' nests. It also hunts small primates and visits villages to steal poultry, which

Fossa

makes it unpopular with the local inhabitants. It is also often shot by hunters, both for its handsome fur and for its meat. In some places it has become rare.

In a rocky lair or a tree hollow the female gives birth to 2—4 young after a gestation period lasting 10 weeks.

BIRDS

VASA PARROT
Coracopsis vasa

The Vasa Parrot, which grows to a length of 50 cm, is found on Madagascar and the Comoro Islands. It lives in lowland forests all around the coast and on mountains up to 1 000 m, and forages in open country. Vasa Parrots are gregarious. Just after dawn flocks of up to 200 birds fly to open savannahs where they search the ground for the seeds of grasses and herbs. Smaller groups fly among the treetops during the day and feed on fruit.

Vasa Parrots make their nests in the hollows of thick branches from September to December. The female lays 3—6 eggs, which she incubates herself while her mate brings food to her. The young are then fed by both parents.

Vasa Parrot

GIANT TORTOISE
Testudo gigantea

The Giant Tortoise is the world's largest tortoise. Its shell is up to 125 cm long, and it weighs over 300 kg. It is an inhabitant of the Seychelles islands, north of Madagascar, and is herbivorous, feeding on grass, berries, green shoots and juicy cacti, though it occasionally eats carrion. These tortoises like to gather at water-holes to drink and bathe, though they can go for months without water and food. The female lays 10—15 hard-shelled eggs and buries them in sandy soil. She flattens the spot with the underneath of her shell, so there is no evidence of her activities, then has nothing more to do with her young. These hatch from the eggs after about 160 days.

MALAGASY GECKO
Phelsuma madagascariensis

The Malagasy Gecko lives on Madagascar and the Seychelles. It grows to a length of up to 30 cm, and lives in trees, darting about the branches and trunks in the daytime, where it catches insects, spiders and other invertebrates. It also likes sweet fruit, and sometimes licks nectar from flowers.
The female usually lays 2 eggs at intervals of 16—30 days, over a period of six months. She places them in a crack in the bark of a tree or in a curled-up leaf. The young mostly hatch after 54—76 days, but sometimes take as long as 120 days.

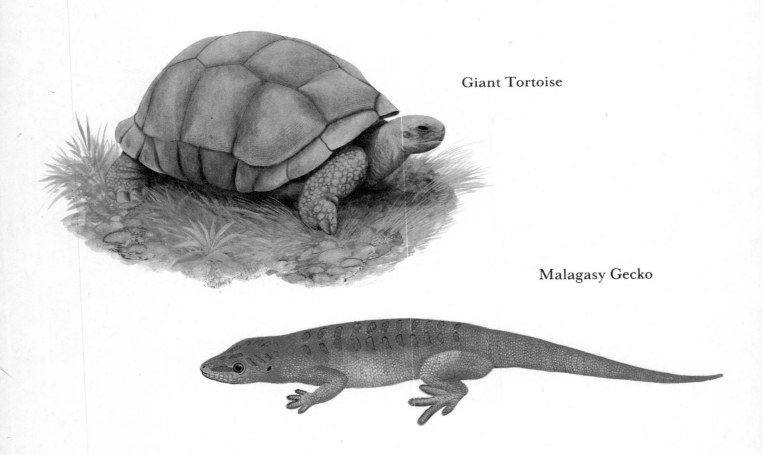

Giant Tortoise

Malagasy Gecko

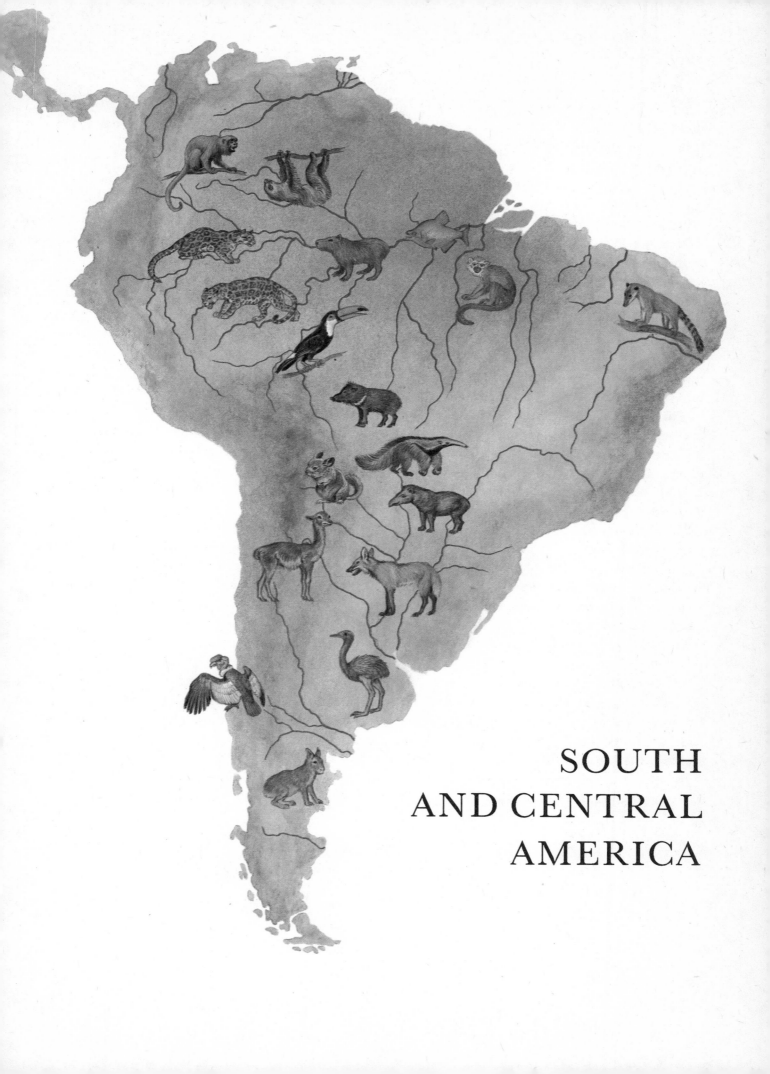

SOUTH
AND CENTRAL
AMERICA

South and Central America together make up a vast area, most of which has a tropical or subtropical climate. This means that it is very hot there all the year round. At noon especially, the sun beats down mercilessly, and all creatures are thankful for the shade of the forests.

Heavy rain is frequent, and torrential downpours often cause disastrous flooding. However, the humidity is good for the vegetation, and the world's greatest forests are to be found in South America. In the Amazon basin alone there is a larger area taken up by rainforests than in all the other continents put together. Even now the rich flora and fauna of South America have not been fully recorded, and each year scientists discover many new species of plants and animals. The number of known South American tree species alone is over 2 500. Many different kinds of beautiful orchids adorn their branches, and vines climb up the trees towards the sun.

There is also an incredible number of animals native to the American tropics, and how many insect species there are can hardly be estimated with any accuracy, though there must be hundreds of thousands of them. The forests teem with life, and from dawn to dusk beautiful birdsong, the harsh cries of parrots and toucans, and the tattoo of woodpeckers come from the heart of the jungle. During the night, different sounds can be heard: roars of great beasts of prey, owls hooting, and frogs croaking.

The original inhabitants of South and Central America are the Indians, many of whom are descended from the legendary Incas or Aztecs. Today most of the Indians live in towns, but in the heart of the Amazon jungles there are still tribes which have never come into contact with civilization. One tribe in particular is famous because its hunters use blowpipes with darts dipped in the terrible poison curare, which is of plant origin, and to which there is no effective antidote.

South America also has some large deserts and semideserts, especially in Peru, Chile and southern Argentina.

A typical feature of the South American landscape is the immense, grassy savannahs with scattered trees, known as the pampas. They are situated in lowland areas where the tropical and subtropical regions meet, so it is always very warm there. Brazilian savannahs with more frequent trees and even sparse forests are called campos, and in the north of Venezuela there are grassy savannahs which are known as llanos.

In the west the South American continent is dominated by the Andes, a tall and extensive range of mountains.

Most of the South American tropics is well supplied with water. The Amazon, the world's greatest river, springs from the eastern slopes of the Andes to flow into the Atlantic Ocean on the opposite side of the continent. Its tributary, the Rio Negro, is also a huge river. In the northern part of the continent the largest river is the Orinoco, and the River Plate, another great river, meets the Atlantic in Argentina.

In contrast, the most southerly parts of South America, Patagonia and Tierra del Fuego, have a very cold climate because they lie very close to the South Pole.

The Forests of South and Central America

The tropical forests of South and Central America provide mankind with a number of important plants. The most useful of these for industry are the rubber trees, whose bark is cut to obtain the sap, or latex, from which rubber is made. These trees are most abundant in Brazil. Another tree of world-wide importance is the cacao, found in the tropics of Central America, whose fruit is used to make cocoa. Both Indians and European settlers benefited from the almost miraculous healing powers of cinchona bark, from which we get the drug quinine. The trees which produce this bark grow in the mountainous forests of the Andes.

The trees of these forests are hung with long lianas, and orchids and bromeliads bloom along their branches and trunks. One remarkable Central American species of bromeliad, the pineapple, grows on the ground, and today it is to be found in tropical plantations throughout the world.

The temperature of the tropical rainforests remains relatively constant at around 27° C, and the humidity among the lush vegetation is always very high.

Photograph by Vladimír Plešinger

105

From Deserts and Savannahs to the Andes

The dry, sandy and stony regions of South and Central America are notable for the large numbers of cacti found there, from tiny species to giants several metres tall. Various species of spurges (low, bush-like or tree-like plants) also push their way to the surface everywhere among the stones. One of the typical plants which is native to the stony areas of Central America is the agave; today it is cultivated in plantations for the long, tough fibres called sisal which come from its crushed leaves. Sisal is extremely strong, and is used in the manufacture of ropes.

Only occasional trees grow in the broad South American savannahs, mostly mimosas and myrtles. Trees and shrubs here do not grow very tall, reaching a height of only 2—6 m, but they are evergreens. Many parts of the savannahs are covered in shrub-like plants and palms.

The majestic Andes mountains are heavily wooded, particularly on their eastern slopes, and in the tropical part of the range there is prolific vegetation up to a height of 5 000 m. Southwards, however, as the climate grows cooler, the peaks become ice-capped; below this there is a band of high pasture, and it is only below this that the mountain forests begin.

Photograph by Vladimír Plešinger

The Aquatic Regions of South and Central America

The great rivers of South America carry more water than any others in the world. During the rainy season they overflow their banks and flood a huge surrounding area—the flood-waters of the Amazon, for example, cover the countryside up to a distance of 100 km. All the rivers in this part of the world are full of fish, and the creeks are inhabited by huge crocodiles and caimans. This is also the home of the world's most powerful snake, the anaconda. One of the largest waterfalls in South America is the Iguaçú Falls on the River Paraná, which pours into a ravine on the borders of Brazil and Argentina.

A characteristic feature of coastal areas is the lagoons surrounded by thick and extensive mangroves. These shallow lakes teem with crabs of many colours—red, blue, yellow and brown. Here the large flocks of ibises, herons and other water-birds and waders are able to find a plentiful supply of food for their young. But there are also clouds of mosquitoes here, whose bites can spread dangerous diseases, such as malaria.

Photograph by Vladimír Plešinger

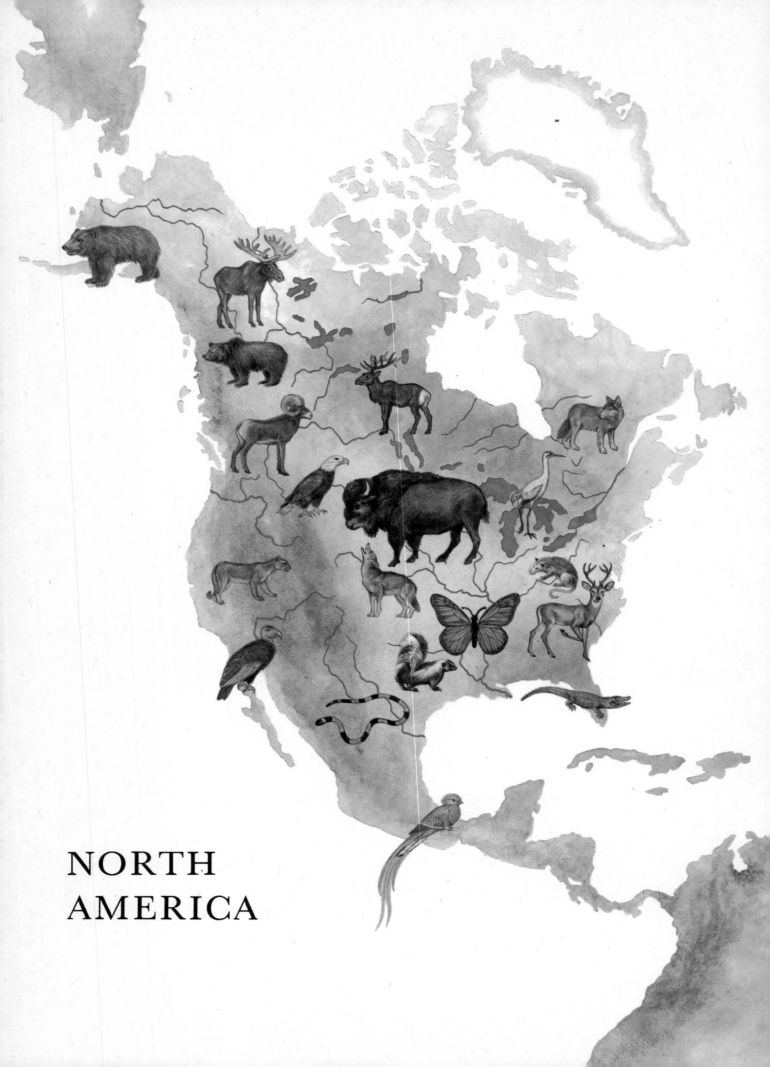

NORTH
AMERICA

The thick forests of **North America** are full of different animals. These provided the original inhabitants, the forest Indians, with food and with skins to make clothes, moccasins and tepees. In the northern part of the continent there are vast stretches of coniferous forest, reaching southwards to the subtropical regions of Florida, Georgia, Alabama and California. The central, north-eastern and south-eastern regions of the United States have mixed forests, while deciduous forests predominate in the central and eastern regions of the country.

The Midwest of the United States is characterized by vast, grassy prairies where the prairie Indians used to roam, hunting the enormous herds of bison. Today most of these prairies have been transformed into cultivated plains where grain and other crops are grown.

North America is crossed by huge mountain chains. The largest of these, the Rocky Mountains, runs right down the west of the continent from Alaska to New Mexico.

Large areas of North America are covered by inhospitable deserts, most of which lie in the south-west. These are dry and hot the whole year round, and in this parched earth cacti, which are well-adapted to the hard conditions, are one of the few plants that can survive. However, the deserts do provide home for many creatures which have the necessary adaptations to survive in an arid environment.

Other parts of the continent have a surplus of water. In the north there are a number of giant lakes, and the rivers are often of huge proportions. The largest of these is the Mississippi, which rises in the area of the Great Lakes. Its chief tributary, the Missouri, is another giant, which rises in the Rocky Mountains, where it is fed by the melting ice of glaciers. In many parts of North America large swamps have been preserved and are now protected as national parks. One of these is the Everglades National Park in Florida.

The northern parts of Canada and Alaska have a very cold climate. The landscape is mostly tundra, which is covered with multi-coloured blossoms during the short northern summer.

The North American Forests

The forests of North America are extremely varied. More than 130 tree species are found there, over twenty of which grow to a huge size. They include the Giant Sequoias of California, the largest trees in the world. These can be about 90 m high, with trunks of as much as 8 m across at the base. The age of these giant trees varies from 3 000 — 3 800 years.

North America has twelve species of true firs alone, and in Canada and central Alaska there are large forests of spruce. A common conifer of the mountainous regions of the north-east is the Eastern Hemlock, growing up to 40 m high. Another typical woodland tree is the larch, which may grow up to 60 m tall, and which loses its needles in winter. There are also many species of broad-leaved deciduous trees — huge oaks, elms, poplars and plane trees (which the Americans call sycamores) all being widespread. Indian hunters had many uses for them. They fashioned their canoes from the bark of one species of North American birch, and obtained a nutritious syrup from the maple.

Photograph by Oldřich Mazůrek

The Prairies, Mountains and Deserts of North America

The original North American prairies stretched from central Canada to Mexico in the south and from Indiana to the Rockies in the west. As far as the eye could see there was tall, lush grass with the occasional low bush. The typical beast of the prairies was the bison, and the million-strong herds of these massive hoofed mammals were hunted by the prairie Indians, who were entirely dependent on them.

The canyons are rocky features peculiar to North America, of which the most famous is the Grand Canyon in Arizona. This is the largest rocky ravine in the world, and is 350 km long, 6—12 km wide and up to 1 600 m deep.

Over a large area stretching from Texas to South California and from Oregon to New Mexico there are both larger and smaller areas of inhospitable desert and semi-desert. Some are sandy, others stony, but even here a large number of cacti grow.

Photograph by Milan Holeček

The Waters and Swamps of North America

The largest and deepest of the Great Lakes is Lake Superior, followed by Lakes Huron and Michigan. The northern Canadian Lakes Great Bear and Great Slave are also among the continent's largest, and both Indian and white fur hunters lived around them.

Evergreen coniferous forests often stretch outwards from the banks of the lakes. Many different species of fish and other water creatures live in the streams, rivers and lakes of the continent, and every year salmon swim high upstream to the unpolluted fast northern rivers to spawn.

Photograph by Oldřich Mazůrek

SOUTH AND CENTRAL AMERICA

MAMMALS

Anteater, Great
Apara or Brazilian Three-banded
    Armadillo
Aperea or Brazilian Cavy
Armadillo, Three-banded or Apara

Bat, Mexican Bulldog
Bat, Vampire
Bear, Spectacled

Capuchin, Brown
Capybara
Cavy, Brazilian or Aperea
Cavy, Patagonian or Mara
Chinchilla
Coatimundi, Red

Deer, Brocket

Guanaco

Jaguar or American Tiger

Mara or Patagonian Cavy
Marmoset, Golden Lion
Monkey, Black Spider
Monkey, Common Squirrel
Monkey, Red Howler

Nutria

Ocelot
Opossum, Philander

Peccary, Collared

Sloth, Three-toed

Tapir, Brazilian
Tiger, American or Jaguar

Uakari, Bald

Wolf, Maned

BIRDS

Condor, Andean
Coquette, Tufted
Curassow, Great

Eagle, Harpy

Flamingo, Andean

Guacharo or Oilbird

Hoatzin

Macaw, Blue-and-Yellow
Macaw, Red-Blue-and-Green

Nandu or Common Rhea

Oilbird or Guacharo
Owl, Spectacled

Parakeet, Monk
Parrot, Yellow-cheeked

Quetzal

Rhea, Common or Nandu

Toucan, Toco

Vulture, South American King
Vulture, Turkey

REPTILES

Anaconda

Basilisk, Plumed

Constrictor, Boa

Snake, Southern Coral

Tortoise, Galápagos Giant

AMPHIBIANS

Frog, Three-striped Arrow Poison

FISH

Eel, Electric

Piranha, Red

INVERTEBRATES

Beetle Dynastes hercules
Butterfly Morpho anaxabia

Spider, Bird-eating
Spider, Tropical Golden Web

NORTH AMERICA

MAMMALS

Antelope, Pronghorn

Bear, American Black
Bear, Grizzly
Bear, Kodiak
Beaver, Canadian
Bison, American

Coyote

Deer, White-tailed or Virginian

Goat, Rocky Mountain

Lion, Mountain or Puma

Mink, American
Moose
Muskrat

Opossum, North American
Otter, Canadian

Puma or Mountain Lion

Raccoon, Ring-tailed

Sheep, Bighorn
Skunk, Common or Striped
Squirrel, American Flying

Wapiti
Wolf

BIRDS

Condor, Californian
Crane, American or Whooping

Duck, Wood

Eagle, Bald

Goose, Canada
Grouse, Sage

Hummingbird, Rufous

Kite, Swallow-tailed

Owl, Burrowing
Owl, Great Horned

Roadrunner

Swan, Trumpeter

Turkey, Wild

Woodpecker, Pileated

REPTILES

Alligator, American

Gila Monster

Rattlesnake, Eastern
    Diamond-backed

Snake, Eastern Coral

INVERTEBRATES

Cicada Killer

Luna or American Moon Moth

Monarch
Moth, American Moon or Luna
Moth, Polyphemus

Spider, Black Widow
Spider, Bolas

THE
FORESTS
OF
SOUTH
AND
CENTRAL
AMERICA

Venezuela, the Caracas region

MAMMALS

PHILANDER OPOSSUM
Caluromys philander

The home of the Philander Opossum is in forests from Venezuela to Brazil. This arboreal marsupial is about 70 cm long, with a hairless tail a little longer than its body, and it lives in the crowns of trees. It climbs deftly among the branches, using its tail as a fifth limb. Hanging by it, like a mountaineer on a rope, it has no trouble in taking birds' eggs from a nest with both its front paws, and it also eats young birds, insects, small tree lizards, frogs and sweet, juicy fruit. They hunt for food after nightfall, spending the day sleeping in the hollows of trees.

The female gives birth to about 7 young. These are poorly developed, being both blind and hairless, but they climb into their mother's pouch and attach themselves to her nipples. It is two months before they grow a coat and leave the pouch, then they cling to their mother's back for several weeks, holding her tail with their own. They become mature at the age of 6—8 months.

VAMPIRE BAT
Desmodus rotundus

Vampires who attack people on dark nights and suck their blood belong to the imaginary world of horror books and films. However, vampires really do exist, but in the form of tiny bats, only 7 cm long. They are found in forest areas from Mexico to Paraguay and northern Chile, along the edges of jungles, and in many places they are indeed the terror of the local animals. They feed on nothing else but blood, flying silently over the ground after nightfall in search of their victims.

During the day vampires sleep in hollow trees or in caves, hundreds often sheltering together in one place. The female gives birth to 1—2 young, which she carries about with her; they cling tightly to her fur during flight.

Philander Opossum

Vampire Bat

Common Squirrel Monkey

Golden Lion Marmoset

GOLDEN LION MARMOSET
Leontideus rosalia

With its huge mane, the Golden Lion Marmoset looks like a miniature lion. This clawed monkey is 65—75 cm long, including its 30-cm tail. It is found, usually living in family groups, in the forests of eastern Brazil, where the animals keep to the tree-tops, moving along the branches with great agility. They hunt insects, spiders and small tree lizards, and also eat the eggs of small bird species and pick fruit, juicy berries and green shoots. At night they sleep in the hollows of trees.

The female usually has 2 offspring, one of which she carries on her stomach, the other on her back. Her mate often carries the young and takes good care of them.

COMMON SQUIRREL MONKEY
Saimiri sciureus

The small Common Squirrel Monkey measures only 40—75 cm, including its tail. It lives in Guyana and Brazil, where it is found in the vast jungles, usually near the banks of rivers and lakes. During the day it runs about the treetops, catching insects and small tree lizards. It is also fond of the eggs and young of birds, but its main food is sweet fruit of various kinds. Squirrel Monkeys usually live in family groups, but they sometimes go about in troops of up to a hundred.

The female has a single offspring, which she carries on her stomach at first, then later on her back.

BALD UAKARI
Cacajao calvus

The Bald Uakari is a strange monkey about 55 cm long which lives in the Amazon rain-

118

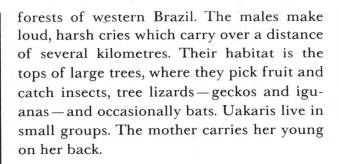

Bald Uakari

Red Howler Monkey

forests of western Brazil. The males make loud, harsh cries which carry over a distance of several kilometres. Their habitat is the tops of large trees, where they pick fruit and catch insects, tree lizards—geckos and iguanas—and occasionally bats. Uakaris live in small groups. The mother carries her young on her back.

RED HOWLER MONKEY
Alouatta seniculus

The Red Howler Monkey gets its name from the loud cries which the male makes. He does this by means of a special vibrating bony drum in his throat, which amplifies the howls. This is a large monkey, which grows up to about 135 cm long, including its tail. It uses this sensitive tail as a fifth limb, often hanging by it.
The Red Howler Monkey is found in Columbia and the central Amazon region, living in the treetops in troops of 20—50

animals. They are vegetarian, feeding entirely on leaves, fruit and shoots. An adult monkey consumes about 1.5 kg of food per day.
The female always gives birth to a single young, which she carries on her back.

BROWN CAPUCHIN
Cebus apella

The Brown Capuchin is an inhabitant of the tropical forests of South America. It lives in trees, but often climbs down to the ground to collect fallen fruit or nuts. These monkeys use large, flat stones on the ground to crack hard nuts. They place a nut on the stone, then take a small pebble in one hand, or a larger one in both, and strike the nut-

119

Brown Capuchin

Black Spider Monkey

shell until it breaks open. Capuchin monkeys are both strong and skilful, and they use their prehensile tails like hands. As well as nuts they eat insects and their larvae, birds' eggs and nestlings. They usually spend the night in hollow trees or among dense branches.

Capuchins usually have a single offspring, rarely twins. The mother carries her young with her everywhere on her back.

BLACK SPIDER MONKEY
Ateles paniscus

The Black Spider Monkey seems to be all arms, legs and tail! It is about 130 cm long, with extremely long limbs, a small head and a prehensile tail measuring more than 70 cm. This tail is very flexible and sensitive, and is used to hang from branches, to pick fruit and to pass food to its mouth. The Black Spider Monkey is a native of the tropical South American forests. It lives in the crowns of trees, and runs along the branches on its hind legs, holding its tail up like a question mark. It can swing by one arm, and then make a flying leap of 10 m or more, catching hold of another branch with its other hand. Spider Monkeys mainly eat leaves, shoots and fruit, occasionally catching insects or small vertebrates.

The Black Spider Monkey has a single young, which the mother at first carries on her chest, then on her back.

RED COATIMUNDI
Nasua nasua

The Red Coatimundi is a bear-like carnivore over 1 m long with a long pointed snout. It lives in the tropical forests of South and Central America, but has also been seen in the south of the United States. It is nimble and quick both in the trees and on the ground, and after dark it darts about its territory, poking its inquisitive nose into crevices and holes. It has an excellent sense of smell, and feeds on insects, molluscs and other invertebrates, birds' eggs and small young mammals. It also eats plants and fallen fruit, and sometimes visits henhouses to steal poultry.

Male Coatimundis are solitary creatures

Red Coatimundi

most of the year, though females often live in small troops. In the shelter of the hollow of a tree or a cave the female gives birth to 2—7 young. They are born blind, and their eyes open at the age of 11 days.

OCELOT
Felis pardalis

The Ocelot reaches a total length of 95—135 cm, though a third of this is taken up by its tail, and it is 50 cm tall at the shoulders. This feline carnivore is found throughout South and Central America and as far as Texas in the United States. It lives in dense forests, where it hunts birds and small arboreal mammals among the treetops. It also preys on rodents and crustaceans on the river banks, and is a good swimmer, often being seen in the water.

In the breeding season the male finds himself a mate, staying with her for a few days. After a gestation period of 70 days the female gives birth to 1—4 young in a safe shelter such as a tree hollow.

JAGUAR or AMERICAN TIGER
Panthera onca

The Jaguar is the biggest of the South American feline carnivores. It reaches a length of 165—240 cm, including its tail, and a weight of more than 130 kg. It is found in South and Central America, and in southern Arizona in the United States. It keeps mostly to the forest, and also frequents river banks with reed beds and tall grass where it can hide easily. Its usual prey are capybaras or young tapirs, but when food is scarce it feeds on small mammals and birds, and fish caught in shallow water. An expert tree climber, it often attacks monkeys.

Ocelot

Jaguar or American Tiger

In the breeding season the male finds himself a mate, with which he lives for a few days. Then he goes off again on his own. In a small cave or a thicket the female gives birth to 1—5 cubs, which stay with their mother for about 2 years.

Three-toed Sloth

THREE-TOED SLOTH
Bradypus tridactylus

The Three-toed Sloth is a native of both South and Central America. It is 50 cm long, and is unusually adapted for life in the treetops. It has 9 neck vertebrae and can turn its head through an angle of 270°. It spends its life hanging upside-down by its strong, curved claws, and its movements are very slow and hesitant. During the day sloths usually sleep, squeezed in the fork of a pair of branches. They set out in search of food after sunset, living mainly on leaves, though they occasionally eat soft stoneless fruit.

During the mating season sloths call out to each other with high-pitched wailing noises. They are solitary animals which separate after the breeding season. The female gives birth to a single young, which clings to its mother's stomach for almost a year.

through thickets, eating fallen fruit, grubbing up roots or munching grass. But Collared Peccaries also hunt reptiles, including venomous snakes. They are protected from the poison fangs by their thick hide covered with bristly hair and by a layer of subcutaneous fat. They also eat molluscs, dead fish thrown up on the bank, and the eggs of water birds.

In the shelter of thick undergrowth, often on a swampy island, the female usually gives birth to twins.

COLLARED PECCARY
Tayassu tajacu

The Collared Peccary is found throughout Central America, as far south as Argentina in South America, and as far north as Texas and Arizona in the United States. It is about 95 cm long, 40 cm tall at the shoulder, and may weigh up to 25 kg. Its favourite haunts are thickets at the edges of thick forests, bushy areas, or swamps on river banks. The animals form small herds which wander

Collared Peccary

123

Brocket Deer

BROCKET DEER
Mazama americana

The Brocket Deer is only 60 cm tall at the shoulders and weighs about 10 kg. It has tiny straight antlers, only 5 cm long and without branches. This deer is a native of dense forests from Guyana to Paraguay. During the day it hides in impenetrable thickets, going out to graze only at dusk. Brocket Deer eat grass, leaves and fallen fruits. They are very shy and wary while feeding, yet they often fall prey to carnivores, large birds of prey and snakes.
Female Brocket Deer usually give birth to a single offspring.

BIRDS

SOUTH AMERICAN KING VULTURE
Sarcorhamphus papa

The South American King Vulture inhabits tropical regions from central Mexico to northern Argentina. This beautifully coloured bird of prey is about 85 cm long, with a wingspan of up to 2 m. It is mostly found in forests or wooded savannahs, mainly in the lowlands, but sometimes in the mountains up to a height of 1 000 — 1 300 m. King Vultures live in pairs. They build their nests in the crowns of tall trees, usually more than 20 m above the ground.

Harpy Eagle

South American King Vulture

The female lays a single off-white egg with russet spots, then both parents take turns to incubate it and also share responsibility for bringing up the young. Adult birds feed mainly on meat from the carcasses of large game, but also hunt small reptiles.

HARPY EAGLE
Harpia harpyja

The Harpy Eagle is the most powerful bird of prey in the world. It is up to 1 m long, with a wingspan of more than 2.5 m. Harpy Eagles also have exceptionally strong feet and huge claws. They are found in the tropics from southern Mexico to eastern Bolivia, living in lowland forests and wooded hills. They are the terror of all monkeys, sloths,

coatimundis, small reptiles and large birds like macaws and toucans.

The Harpy Eagle's nest is built of strong branches in the treetops, up to 60 m high, and is lined with green leaves. The female lays 1—2 eggs.

GREAT CURASSOW
Crax rubra

The Great Curassow is a heavily-built, fowl-like bird, up to 90 cm in length. It is found in the extensive tropical forests from Mexico to western Ecuador. These birds spend most of the day in the trees, pecking at shoots, berries and seeds, and they also catch insects and small arboreal reptiles. Curassows build themselves flat nests of

125

Great Curassow

Hoatzin

twigs and leaves high in the trees. The female lays 2 eggs, the size of goose eggs, and incubates the clutch herself. When the young hatch they leap down to the ground from the nest, which may be 6—30 m above the ground. There they hide in thickets with their mother for several days, and at the age of 4 days they begin to fly. After a week they can fly up to low branches to roost.

HOATZIN
Opisthocomus hoazin

The Hoatzin is a curious bird which is found in the tropical forests of South America around the Andes. It grows to 55—60 cm. The Hoatzin's crop is divided in two, half to store food, half to pre-digest it. The bird feeds exclusively on plant material, particularly the leaves of mangroves and arum plants.

Hoatzins build untidy nests of twigs on strong horizontal branches 2—6 m above the ground, and usually overhanging water. This protects them from predators. The birds nest in colonies, one male having several mates. Each hen lays 2—4 eggs in her own nest, and incubates them herself. At birth the young are naked, but can see immediately and are very mobile. On the tip of each wing they have two toes with claws, which they use to grasp branches as they creep from the nest. After three weeks, however, these claws fall off, and the toes become stunted and gradually disappear.

BLUE-AND-YELLOW MACAW
Ara ararauna

The Blue-and-Yellow Macaw, a large parrot about 85 cm long, is found from Panama to Bolivia. It usually lives on the outskirts of forests along river banks. Outside the mating season macaws fly about the treetops in flocks, in search of palm nuts,

juicy fruit, berries and seeds. They sometimes eat large insects.

The female lays 2 eggs in a dead palm
trunk. She incubates them herself, while her
mate feeds her on food regurgitated from
his crop. Both parents look after the young,
which leave the nest after 13 weeks.

RED-BLUE-AND-GREEN MACAW
Ara chloroptera

The Red-Blue-and-Green Macaw is found
in the South American forests from Panama
to northern Argentina and south-eastern
Brazil. It grows up to 90 cm in length, and
is one of the largest parrots. These macaws
gather in small flocks, though in the nesting
season they live in pairs. The female lays
2 eggs in the hollow of a tree, incubating
them herself. The Red-Blue-and-Green
Macaw lives on green shoots, seeds and
various soft fruits.

MONK PARAKEET
Myiopsitta monachus

The Monk Parakeet occurs in eastern Bolivia, Paraguay, Brazil and central Argentina.
These birds grow to a length of about
30 cm. They live in large flocks, even in the

Blue-and-Yellow Macaw

Monk Parakeet

Red-Blue-and-Green Macaw

Yellow-cheeked Parrot

Spectacled Owl

nesting season, when colonies consist of 50—70 pairs of birds. The nests are built so closely together on the branches that they combine to form a huge construction, sometimes weighing over a tonne. Tirelessly, they carry in their beaks thin twigs up to 2.5 m in length, which then they weave together to make the nest. Each pair has its own small compartment, where the female lays 5—7 eggs; when the chicks hatch they are fed by both parents. Monk Parakeets feed on seeds, green shoots and soft fruit.

YELLOW-CHEEKED PARROT
Amazona autumnalis

The Yellow-cheeked Parrot is found from south-eastern Mexico to north-western Brazil. It grows to a length of about 35 cm. Yellow-cheeked Parrots are forest dwellers, but often fly into nearby fruit plantations; mostly, however, they eat seeds, shoots and berries and also insects.

In the nesting season these birds live in pairs. The female lays 2—4 eggs in an un-lined tree hollow, then incubates them herself. Both parents then feed the young, which fly from the nest at the age of 65 days.

SPECTACLED OWL
Pulsatrix perspicillata

The Spectacled Owl, which is about 45 cm long, occurs from southern Mexico to Argentina and Bolivia, where its favourite haunts are damp lowland woods and river banks. Here it likes to catch crabs, seizing them when they crawl out of the water. They also hunt small mammals, young iguanas and large insects.

In a hollow in a tree the female lays 2 eggs, which she incubates herself. During this time she is fed by her mate, and the male continues to bring food for the whole family during the first 10 days of nest care. After about 35 days the young owls leave the nest and perch on the surrounding branches. In another 14 days they begin to fly and learn to hunt.

Oilbird or Guacharo

Tufted Coquette

OILBIRD or GUACHARO
Steatornis caripensis

The Oilbird, or Guacharo, is a remarkable relative of the nightjars, and is 43 cm long. It is found in mountain forests in Guyana, Venezuela, Colombia, Ecuador and Peru, living in large communities deep inside caves. During the day the birds remain hidden in the darkest corners, where light never penetrates. Though they fly about in complete darkness, among projecting rocks and winding tunnels, they never crash into the walls. This is because they, like bats, can send out high-pitched signals, which bounce off the objects in front of them and act as radar.

At twilight flocks of Oilbirds leave the caves and set off together to find food. They live almost exclusively on the fruit of the oil palm.

Oilbirds also nest in the caves, in large colonies. Their nests are made in crevices in the rocks, from crushed fruit stuck together with sticky saliva. The female lays 2—4 eggs, which both parents incubate. They also share in the feeding of the young, which stay in the nest until they are about 120 days old.

TUFTED COQUETTE
Lophornis ornata

The Tufted Coquette is a beautiful hummingbird that is only 7 cm long and inhabits the forest regions of Venezuela, Guyana and Trinidad. During the rainy season the aggressive male performs colourful nuptial displays to attract the female. Then, when mating is over, he leaves his mate and looks for a new one while the female builds her nest.

Using fine vegetable fibres, spiders' webs and pieces of bark and lichen, the female makes a small, basket-shaped nest on a branch. She lays 2 eggs, and later feeds the young on a mixture of honey and small insects from her crop. In 3 weeks the young birds leave the nest and look after themselves. Coquettes hover beside flowers to suck out the sweet nectar, and catch insects in mid-flight.

TOCO TOUCAN
Ramphastos toco

The Toco Toucan reaches a length of about 65 cm. It has a gigantic beak, containing many tiny chambers filled with air, which

Toco Toucan

makes it very light for its size. Toco Toucans live in the vast forests from Guyana to northern Argentina. They spend most of their time in the treetops, where they pick sweet fruit or ripening berries. They also catch young iguanas and eat birds' eggs, insects and invertebrates. They find large hollows or dense foliage in which to shelter from their enemies during the night.

The birds nest in holes in trees. The female lays 2 eggs, taking turns with her mate to incubate them. The parents then feed their young with crushed fruit and insects for about 7 weeks until the young toucans leave the nest and fly with their parents.

REPTILES

PLUMED BASILISK
Basiliscus plumifrons

In its native Costa Rica the Plumed Basilisk is feared, because the local Indians believe it is a supernatural creature made up of several other kinds of animals. If seen close to a human dwelling it supposedly predicts the death of one of the occupants. In fact these sociable creatures are quite harmless. They usually live in bushes and trees beside rivers. When in danger they dive into the

Plumed Basilisk

Boa Constrictor

Southern Coral Snake

water, escaping their enemies easily beneath the surface. Basilisks eat sweet fruit, insects and small vertebrates.

The female lays and incubates her eggs in a hole in soft soil. The young are shaped like their parents.

BOA CONSTRICTOR
Boa constrictor

The Boa Constrictor is one of the best-known venomless snakes. It usually grows to a length of 4 m, and the largest specimen ever measured was 5.6 m. Boa Constrictors are found in the forests and bush of South and Central America. During the day they remain hidden in caves or rocky crevices or among tree roots. After sunset they set out to hunt their prey, usually waiting for them on trees. Boas grasp their prey with their fangs, then choke their victims to death by squeezing them, afterwards swallowing them whole. They mostly eat small mammals and birds.

The female gives birth to about 30 live young in a sheltered spot. The Boa Constrictor has an average lifespan of 20—30 years.

SOUTHERN CORAL SNAKE
Micrurus frontalis

The Southern Coral Snake is one of the most colourful of all snakes, but also one of the most venomous. It is found in forest areas of Brazil, Paraguay, Uruguay and northern Argentina. During the day this timid snake hides beneath a stone or under the bark of a tree stump, hunting for food after dark. It glides through crevices and hollows in search of small lizards or other snakes. It grasps the prey and bites into it, injecting venom from its fangs. The poison acts very rapidly, and the Coral Snake swallows its victim whole.

The female lays about 10 eggs in a hole in the ground or between the roots of a tree. The young hatch after 3 months.

131

AMPHIBIANS

THREE-STRIPED ARROW POISON FROG
Dendrobates trivittatus

The Three-striped Arrow Poison Frog is a small tree frog about 4 cm long. It lives in the primary forests from Peru to the Amazon region, and eats insects, their larvae and spiders. This colourful creature has a very effective skin poison which causes muscle paralysis if it gets into the bloodstream through even a tiny scratch. Indians obtain a poison for the tips of their blowpipe darts from this frog, which is how the creature got its name. Not surprisingly it seldom falls prey to other animals.

The female lays 6—8 eggs in a damp spot on land. The male then waits patiently beside the clutch for a full two weeks, until the tadpoles hatch. These immediately climb on to their father's back and attach themselves to his skin by means of suckers on their mouths. The male frog then carries his young about with him everywhere, dipping them in water from time to time. When the tadpoles are 14 days old, the adult finds a patch of still, shallow water. There the tadpoles release themselves and continue their development. After a further 6 weeks their metamorphosis is complete, and they leave the water as small frogs.

Three-striped Arrow Poison Frog

INVERTEBRATES

BIRD-EATING SPIDER
Avicularia avicularia

The body of the huge Bird-eating Spider is 5—6 cm long. Its massive size, hairy body and legs and huge jaws can easily frighten people, but in fact the Bird-eating Spider is not dangerous to man. It is not aggressive and bites only in self-defence. Its venom is very weak, and will not even kill a small animal. It hunts at night, mostly catching insects and their larvae, though adult spiders also eat small geckos, frogs, lizards and small young birds.

In a spun cocoon the female lays 100—200 eggs. The young spiders hatch after 25 days, but stay in the cocoon for another 20 days before biting their way out.

TROPICAL GOLDEN WEB SPIDER
Nephila clavipes

The Tropical Golden Web Spider lives in the tropics of South and Central America. The female reaches a length of 25 mm, while the tiny male measures only 4 mm. These spiders spin a large web of over 1 m

in diameter in the forest between tree trunks. The web is so strong that small birds often get caught in it, but Golden Web Spiders only eat small insects. The natives use the strong webs for catching small fish. The female lays her eggs in a cocoon. The young are born after a few days and crawl off into the surrounding area.

BEETLE
Dynastes hercules

The *Dynastes hercules* is one of the largest beetles in the world. The male may be up to 17 cm long, including its horn, while the female, which has no horn, is only 9 cm in length. These beetles are found in tropical regions of Central America living in deciduous forests, where the female lays her eggs

in rotten tree stumps. There the larvae grow to a length of 12 cm, and even at the pupa stage the males' horns can be seen clearly.

BUTTERFLY
Morpho anaxabia

Morpho anaxabia is a beautiful butterfly of the Brazilian forests with a wingspan of about 14 cm. During the day it flies high above the treetops, flying down in the morning to drink at puddles. It is always very wary, and is not easily caught.

Beetle *Dynastes hercules*

Butterfly *Morpho anaxabia*

Foothills of the Andes — the Venezuelan "llanos"

FROM DESERTS AND SAVANNAHS TO THE ANDES

MAMMALS

SPECTACLED BEAR
Tremarctos ornatus

With its characteristic eye markings the Spectacled Bear really does look as though it is wearing glasses. This is the only South American bear, and it lives in the equatorial region of the Andes, from Venezuela to Peru and Chile, in dense mountain forests. It is a small bear, about 150 cm long and 60 cm tall at the shoulders. It spends the day in caves, setting out after dark to patrol its territory in search of food. Its usual diet consists of small vertebrates, insects and fruit. It is also fond of honey and often breaks open the nests of wild bees, climbing trees to get at them.

In a softly lined den the female gives birth to 1 or, more rarely, up to 3 blind, sparsely furred cubs, which she looks after for 2 years.

MANED WOLF
Chrysocyon brachyurus

The Maned Wolf roams the broad pampas of South America from Brazil to northern Argentina. This canine carnivore is 75 cm tall at the shoulders and weighs over 20 kg. Its favourite haunts are marshland and lakes rimmed with thick vegetation, where it pushes its way deftly through the bushes or reeds in search of prey. It attacks agoutis and small birds, and catches frogs, crustaceans and fish in shallow water. Maned Wolves also eat fallen fruit. They prowl both in daylight and after dark, sleeping at night in caves, thickets or hollow trees, where the female gives birth to 1 — 5 young.

GREAT ANTEATER
Myrmecophaga tridactyla

The Great Anteater lives in arid bushland from Guatemala to Argentina. It is a large

Spectacled Bear

Maned Wolf

animal, weighing up to 50 kg. It is some 2.3 m long, including its 1-m-long bushy tail. The Great Anteater wakes up after dark and sets out to feed. With its powerful, sharp, pointed claws it digs out anthills or termitaria. It waits for the excited ants or termites to rush out, then it pushes out its long, sticky tongue, collecting hundreds of insects on it at a time. It swallows them whole, since it has no teeth at all, and they are crushed in its stomach by friction of the muscular walls which turns the food into pulp.

In the mating season the male stays with his mate for a short time only. The mother carries her single offspring with her on her back wherever she goes.

APARA or BRAZILIAN THREE-BANDED ARMADILLO
Tolypeutes tricinctus

The Apara, or Brazilian Three-banded Armadillo, is an inhabitant of bushland in Brazil. It is only 30 cm long, and remains hidden in the daytime among boulders or in

Great Anteater

Apara or Brazilian Three-banded Armadillo

holes between roots of trees and bushes. After dark it scuttles about the ground in search of worms, molluscs and insects, which it traces with its excellent sense of smell. Aparas also occasionally eat small lizards, birds' eggs and fallen berries. When danger threatens they roll into a complete ball. The sections of the body armour or carapace and those on the head fit tightly together, forming a perfectly closed ball and hiding the animal's soft underbelly, snout and tail.

The female has a single young.

MARA or PATAGONIAN CAVY
Dolichotis patagona

The Mara, or Patagonian Cavy, is a large rodent, about 50 cm tall. It is a native of the

Aperea or Brazilian Cavy

dry, grassy savannahs and semideserts of Patagonia. Maras live in small groups, setting out to graze after sunrise. They eat grass, herbs, leaves and soft twigs.

The female digs a burrow in the ground, where she gives birth to 1—3 offspring.

APEREA or BRAZILIAN CAVY
Cavia aperea

That familiar pet, the guinea-pig, originally came from South America. Its ancestor, the Aperea, or Brazilian Cavy, lives in lowlands and mountains from Guyana to Argentina. Apereas grow up to 30 cm long and 0.5 kg in weight. They are found in grasslands, plains and bushy areas, usually in large

Mara or Patagonian Cavy

colonies. They eat grass, shoots, bark, fruit and seeds, and also like the occasional mollusc or insect.

The female gives birth several times a year, mostly to twins. The young are sighted at birth, and before long are very active.

CHINCHILLA
Chinchilla laniger

The Chinchilla has the finest fur of all the mammals, for which reason it has been prized since ancient times. However, since Chinchillas grow to a length of only 40 cm, 12 cm of which is taken up by their tails, it takes over a hundred pelts to make a single fur coat. Even in the days of the Incas this fur was used to make special garments for rulers and priests, so Chinchillas are now extinct in many areas. At present, Chinchillas occur in the wild only in the mountains of Bolivia, though they were previously common in Peru and Chile. They are bred on farms throughout the world, but are not very prolific.

Chinchillas live in pairs throughout the year, and the female usually gives birth to twins annually. These animals set out from their rocky shelters or burrows in search of food only after dark, and live on grass, shoots and roots.

Chinchilla

GUANACO
Lama guanicoe

The Guanaco is the forerunner of the Llama, a domesticated animal used as a beast of burden among the Indians of the Andes mountains. It is 90—130 cm tall at the shoulders and weighs 60—75 kg. Its home is in the rocky, mountainous areas of the Andes from northern Peru to Tierra del Fuego. Guanacos live in small herds, led by a strong male which stands guard near the grazing animals. When he senses danger he warns the herd and they rush to safety. Guanacos feed on grass, leaves, shoots of bushes and various fruits.

Guanaco

BIRDS

COMMON RHEA or NANDU
Rhea americana

The Common Rhea, or Nandu, roams through grassy and bushy pampas from north-eastern Brazil to central Argentina. It is a large bird which cannot fly, and grows to a height of 150 cm and a weight of about 25 kg. Outside the nesting season Nandus wander through the countryside in small flocks, foraging for grass, the leaves of bushes or fallen fruit, and also catching insects and small vertebrates.

The nest is built by the male on the ground amid tall grass. It consists of a shallow hole, sparsely lined with stalks and leaves, and several females usually lay their eggs in the same nest. A full clutch consists of 12—30 yellowish eggs, which are incubated by the male, who also looks after the young.

ANDEAN CONDOR
Vultur gryphus

The condor is the world's largest bird of prey, weighing as much as 12 kg and having a wingspan of up to 3.2 m. Condors are found in the Andes from western Venezuela to Argentina, and also on coastal cliffs as far away as Patagonia. They often circle above valleys and ravines for hours on end in search of prey, and usually eat the meat of large mammals which have died or been killed, especially llamas.

Pairs of Andean Condors build their nests on inaccessible rocky ledges, and line them with scraps of hide from dead mammals. The female lays a single egg, which the parents take turns to incubate. Both birds also feed the young, which flies from the nest 6 months later.

TURKEY VULTURE
Cathartes aura

The Turkey Vulture is one of the most common American birds of prey. It is found from southern Canada to the southern tip of South America and the Falkland Islands, and is most widespread in the tropics. It is 75 cm long with a wingspan of 180 cm. Turkey Vultures gather in large flocks, flying into towns to look for rubbish and

Common Rhea or Nandu

Andean Condor

scraps of meat. Their main food is fresh animal carcasses, but they also like to gather up the remains of fishermen's catches and eat eggs and fruit.

The nest is usually built in a small cave high on a rock face, and is lined with pieces of hide from carcasses. The female lays 2—3 eggs, taking turns with her mate to incubate them. Both parents bring food for the young in their crops.

QUETZAL
Pharomachrus mocinno

The Quetzal was one of the sacred birds of the Aztecs. Its beautiful feathers were prized above gold, and the powerful ruler would order anyone who killed the bird to be put to death. The Aztecs, who lived in what is now Mexico, worshipped a powerful god called Quetzalcoatl. According to their legends he was a feathered snake, and his feathers were those of the Quetzal.

This bird lives in the mountains of humid tropical forests from Mexico to Panama. It grows to a length of about 36 cm, but in the mating season the male is adorned with

Turkey Vulture

Quetzal

magnificent tail feathers which may be over 60 cm long. Quetzals live in the crowns of trees, eating soft fruit or catching insects, spiders and small geckos.

These birds usually nest in holes in trees abandoned by woodpeckers. In a nest lined with slivers of rotten wood the female lays 2—4 eggs, taking turns with her mate to incubate them. Both birds also feed the young for the month they spend in the nest before flying.

REPTILES

GALÁPAGOS GIANT TORTOISE
Testudo elephantopus

The Galápagos Giant Tortoise is one of the largest of all tortoises. It may weigh as much as 250 kg, and sometimes lives to be 200 years old. Their home is the Galápagos Islands, which are in the Pacific, 1 000 km off the coast of Ecuador. There were once vast numbers of them on the islands, but they were almost completely wiped out by sailors who killed them in their hundreds for meat.

These giant tortoises live on the juicy fruit of cacti, and on grass and the leaves of shrubs. They often make trips lasting several days to get to freshwater springs inland where they drink and bathe. In October the female usually lays several dozen eggs in holes dug in the ground. The young are able to fend for themselves immediately when they hatch.

Galápagos Giant Tortoise

THE
AQUATIC
REGIONS
OF
SOUTH
AND
CENTRAL
AMERICA

———

Photograph by Vladimír Plešinger

The Orinoco

144

MAMMALS

MEXICAN BULLDOG BAT
Noctilio leporinus

The strange Mexican Bulldog Bat is found throughout the tropical regions of South America. It has a wingspan of 45 cm, and is expert at catching fish. After sunset it flies out from its shelter in tree hollows and skims over the surface of the water. As it flies it dips its long toes, with their strong, curved claws, into the water and plucks out small fish. It then flies up in the air and eats its prey as it flutters along. Like other bats, it also catches flying insects.

The female carries her young clinging to the hair on her chest as she flies.

CAPYBARA
Hydrochoerus hydrochaeris

The Capybara is the largest rodent in the world. It grows to a height of over 50 cm, and weighs over 50 kg. Its home is the tropical regions from Panama to north-western Argentina, where it lives in dense vegetation around rivers and lakes. Small herds of Capybaras remain hidden in the day-time, going out to look for food after dark. They eat various plants, bark and fallen fruit. When danger threatens they hide in rivers, and are excellent swimmers.

A single male has several mates, and the female gives birth to between 2 and 8 young hidden in thick vegetation; these are able to see at birth.

NUTRIA
Myocastor coypus

The Nutria is a sturdy South American rodent, with a body 40—80 cm long and a tail 40—50 cm long, and it weighs up to 9 kg. It frequents river banks, where it digs burrows or builds nests in beds of reeds. It gets most of its food from the water, diving to the bottom and digging up the roots and stems of

Mexican Bulldog Bat

Nutria

145

Capybara

aquatic plants. On land it eats grass, the bark of young trees, and fallen fruit.

The female has 1—10 young twice a year in her riverside lair. They are sighted at birth.

BRAZILIAN TAPIR
Tapirus terrestris

The Brazilian Tapir is found from Mexico to northern Argentina, and is up to 1 m tall and 2 m long. It lives in marshland overgrown with vegetation, in swamps or along the banks of rivers. These tapirs are excellent swimmers and divers. During the day they rest, hidden in reeds or thickets. They come out after sunset and always use the same well-trodden tracks. First they go in the water, where they often remain for hours, then they eat leaves, grass, tree bark and fallen fruit.

Tapirs are solitary animals, finding themselves mates only in the breeding season. The female has a single young.

Brazilian Tapir

146

BIRDS

ANDEAN FLAMINGO
Phoenicoparrus andinus

The beautifully coloured Andean Flamingo lives beside salty mountain lakes from south-western Peru to the north of Chile and Argentina. In the shallow waters of these lakes, at a height of up to 4 500 m above sea level, these flamingoes feed on red algae, which are present in such quantities that they turn the water red. They also eat small aquatic invertebrates, which they filter through a network of fine grooves along the sides of their beaks.

Little is known of the nesting habits of this species. Despite the remoteness of its nesting sites, the Andean Flamingo is not safe from man. The Indians collect both eggs and chicks and catch the adult birds during the moulting period. Very often whole colonies of these beautiful birds are quickly destroyed.

Andean Flamingo

REPTILES

ANACONDA
Eunectes murinus

The Anaconda is the largest snake in the world. It sometimes grows to over 9 m in

length, and weighs around 150 kg. It occurs mainly in the Amazon basin, and spends

Anaconda

most of its time in or near the water, where it hunts capybaras, young tapirs and other mammals. It chokes its prey to death in the coils of its massive muscular body, then swallows it whole.

The female can give birth to as many as 70 live young. These are about 90 cm long and completely independent.

FISH

RED PIRANHA
Serrasalmus nattereri

A 35-cm-long fish found in South American rivers, the Piranha is famous for its predatory behaviour. It is dreaded by all animals including humans, because it preys on every living thing it encounters. Piranhas attack in shoals, quickly biting out pieces of skin and flesh with their sharp, forward-pointing teeth, leaving only the skeleton. Some South American Indian tribes carry out ritual burials, sinking their dead in baskets into water rich in piranhas, and then taking out the skeletons to bury them. This often helps prevent the spread of infectious diseases. Piranhas, which live in large shoals, spawn among water plants and roots close to the bank.

ELECTRIC EEL
Electrophorus electricus

The Electric Eel is a living, swimming power station. It generates electricity by means of a special organ which occupies four-fifths of its body. It can produce a powerful shock, enough to kill small animals and to stun or paralyze larger ones. Electric Eels are up to 2.9 m long and eat only small prey, mainly fish. These they kill with a discharge of 300—600 volts.

Red Piranha

Electric Eel

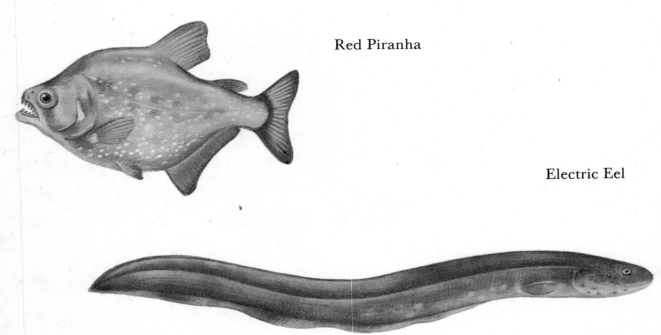

THE
NORTH
AMERICAN
FORESTS

The Rocky Mountains, Jasper National Park

MAMMALS

NORTH AMERICAN OPOSSUM
Didelphis marsupialis

The North American Opossum is distributed all over the eastern and central United States, and in Central America. It grows to a length of 90 cm, though 40 cm of this is its prehensile tail. Opossums usually live in forests, and near human settlements, where they go at night to steal poultry. But their main food is small mammals, birds' eggs, amphibians, molluscs and insects, and they are also fond of sweet, juicy fruit.

The female makes a round nest of leaves and thin twigs in a sheltered place. Here she has 8—16 young, which are only 1 cm long and weigh 2 g. The blind, naked offspring find their way by instinct into their mother's pouch, where they remain and develop for three months. The mother carries the half-grown young on her back.

North American Opossum

AMERICAN BLACK BEAR
Ursus americanus

The American Black Bear is found in Canada and the north of the United States, the south-eastern states and Mexico. It grows to a height of 1 m at the shoulders and a weight of 150 kg. Black Bears roam through their territory, hunting small vertebrates on land and fishing in shallow waters. They also feed on molluscs, insects and forest fruit. In national parks they are a great tourist attraction. They come right

American Black Bear

Grizzly Bear

up to the road, stopping cars and begging for sweets from the occupants.

Black Bears hibernate in winter in caves or in hollows under uprooted trees. Here the females give birth to their young in January or Feburary. They usually have 2 cubs, or sometimes up to 4. These cubs open their eyes after 28—38 days, and it is 2 months before the mother leads them from the den for the first time. They stay with their mother for 2 years.

GRIZZLY BEAR
Ursus horribilis

The Grizzly Bear can grow up to 2.5 m long and weigh over 300 kg. Among the American Indians it used to be a symbol of courage and strength, and Indian braves made necklaces from its powerful claws to mark their bravery in attacking and killing this bear.
In many parts of North America the grizzly is now extinct. It is mostly found in Canada,

Alaska and the mountains of Montana. Grizzly Bears usually hunt for their food after sunset, and their prey include large stags, birds and reptiles. When the salmon are running they fish in mountain pools during the day, and also eat forest fruit and honey.
The grizzly hibernates in winter in its den; here the female also gives birth to 2—3 cubs in January or February.

KODIAK BEAR
Ursus arctos middendorfii

The Kodiak Bear is the largest carnivore in the world. It can weigh over 1 tonne, and measure up to 3 m long. It inhabits the island of Kodiak, off the west coast of Alaska, and the western part of the Alaskan peninsula. It lives in the forest, and builds its den in a cave or beneath the roots of a large tree at the end of October. Here it sleeps out the long and frosty winter. In December or Jan-

Ring-tailed Raccoon

uary the female gives birth to 1—6 cubs inside this den. The playful cubs leave the nest for the first time at the age of 45 days. In spring the Kodiak Bears leave their winter home a good deal thinner than when they entered it, for they have eaten nothing all winter. They look for the carcasses of large animals which have not survived the winter frosts and blizzards. They also feed on plants and on the eggs of the wild ducks and geese which nest in the far north. At the end of June and the beginning of July the Kodiak Bears have a real feast when the salmon swim up to the cold, clear mountain streams to spawn, and the massive bears become fishermen for a week or two.

RING-TAILED RACCOON
Procyon lotor

The Ring-tailed Raccoon lives in mixed and deciduous woodlands in the United States and northern Mexico where there are abundant rivers or lakes. This bear-like carnivore with a bushy tail is about 1 m long. During the day it usually sleeps in a hole in a tree or in the abandoned nest of a bird of prey.

Kodiak Bear

Wolf

After dark it climbs over trees and scurries along the ground, or wades through shallow water. Using its sense of smell it finds birds' nests and steals the young or eggs. It also catches frogs, fish and molluscs, and sometimes takes hens from poultry-sheds on the outskirts of towns and villages. It eats sweet fruit from the forest, too. Raccoons often

American Flying Squirrel

wash their prey carefully in water before eating it.

In a burrow the female gives birth to 1—7 young.

WOLF
Canis lupus

In North America the Wolf is found from Alaska to northern Mexico, and it also lives in parts of Europe and Asia. The biggest specimens from Alaska and Canada reach a height of 100 cm at the shoulders and a weight of about 75 kg. Wolves are mostly found in vast forests and bushland. In February, when the mating season begins, the forests start to ring with their long-drawn-out howls, then in April or May the female gives birth to 5—7 cubs in an underground lair. Three weeks later these are padding about playfully. When the cubs are older, the parent wolves take their voracious offspring hunting with them, and individual families combine to make up larger packs in which the wolves hunt in winter. Such packs hunt large animals such as moose or reindeer, and if they are very hungry they attack stray cattle. In the summer wolves mainly eat rodents, birds and lizards, and also sweet woodland fruit.

White-tailed or Virginian Deer

AMERICAN FLYING SQUIRREL
Glaucomys volans

The American Flying Squirrel is an inhabitant of the huge forests in the east of the United States. This small rodent is 25 cm long in all, and 10 cm of this is its tail. It has a large fold of skin on its back, which it can spread like a parachute and glide through the air for distances of up to 30 m. Flying Squirrels rest in the hollows of trees in the daytime, searching for food in the treetops after dark. They eat insects, birds' eggs, nuts and various kinds of fruit.
The female has young twice a year, 3—6 in each litter.

WHITE-TAILED or VIRGINIAN DEER
Odocoileus virginianus

The White-tailed or Virginian Deer is very common from southern Canada to Mexico, where it lives in herds in forests and sometimes in bushy areas. The male grows to a height of 110 cm at the shoulders and a weight of 200 kg. The female is smaller, without antlers. This deer lives on leaves, twigs, grass and various fruits.
The female has 1 or occasionally 2 young. The young deer is born with open eyes and is able to walk, though it remains lying in a sheltered place for 5—10 days while the mother comes to suckle it. After 10 days the beautifully spotted young deer follows its mother, who continues to suckle it for 1—2 months.

WAPITI
Cervus canadensis

The Wapiti was a favourite game animal of the North American Indians from southwestern Canada to New Mexico, but was hunted to extinction in many areas. This huge deer, 150 cm tall at the shoulders and weighing over 300 kg, is found in mountain forests, though in winter it goes down to the shelter of the valleys. It feeds on grass, leaves, twigs, bark and woodland fruit.
At the end of August stags fight duels for the possession of herds of females. In May the females give birth to 1 or occasionally 2 young.

MOOSE
Alces alces

The Moose is a species of deer typical of the

Wapiti

broad forest tracts of Alaska, Canada and the north-eastern and north-western regions of the United States, though it also occurs in the northern parts of Europe and Asia. The largest Alaskan Moose reach a height of 2.35 m at the shoulders and a weight of over 500 kg. Males have antlers which are up to 160 cm across and may weigh 20 kg. These antlers have as many as 30 tines, the shape differing from animal to animal. Ma-

Moose

ture males shed their antlers in November or December. The favourite haunts of Moose are sparsely wooded areas of mixed or deciduous trees, near lakes or rivers. They are good swimmers, able to cross even large rivers easily, and they sometimes go under water. Moose obtain most of their food from shallow water, where they eat aquatic and marsh plants. They also eat grass, lichen, leaves, and the peeled-off bark of trees.

Adult males battle over the females, then in May or June females have 1 or sometimes 2 young.

BIRDS

SWALLOW-TAILED KITE
Elanoides forficatus

The Swallow-tailed Kite is widespread from the east of the United States to northern Argentina, mainly in pine forests and swampland. This slender bird of prey, some 55 cm long with a wingspan of 130 cm, flies gracefully through the air catching insects, which it swallows in mid-air. It occasionally catches small fish in shallow water.

A pair of Swallow-tailed Kites build their nest in the crown of a tall tree. Small twigs for making the nest are collected in flight. In the soft lining of this nest the female lays 2—4 eggs, which she incubates herself.

WILD TURKEY
Meleagris gallopavo

The Wild Turkey, up to 85 cm long, is a native of parts of the central, southern, eastern and north-eastern United States and Mexico. However, its distribution is discontinuous, and it can no longer be found in many places, such as Georgia and Carolina. It lives in open woodland or forest clearings, but flies to nearby fields in search of food, and eats grain, berries, fruit, green

Wild Turkey

Swallow-tailed Kite

157

Great Horned Owl

parts of plants, insects, spiders and molluscs. Adult birds sometimes catch small reptiles and rodents.

At the end of February the turkeycocks gather in clearings to make their courting display and attract the hens' attention. For a nest the females scratch out a shallow depression beneath a fallen tree trunk or in thick bushes, lining this with blades of grass and leaves. Here they lay 9—12 eggs. The day after hatching the chicks set off with their mother in search of food.

GREAT HORNED OWL
Bubo virginianus

The Great Horned Owl is the largest of the American owls and grows to a length of 55 cm, with a wingspan of 135 cm. It is found from Alaska to Brazil, mostly in woodlands and forests, and also in rocky areas, bushland and prairies. It normally stays in the same place throughout the year. It hunts after dark, preying on ground squirrels, rabbits and mice, and catching small reptiles and birds. It occasionally fishes in shallow water, and often catches insects.

Between January and March the female lays her 2—3 eggs in a nest abandoned by a bird of prey, on the floor of a rocky cave or in a tree hollow. She incubates them herself, while her mate provides her with food, then after the young have hatched both parents feed them.

RUFOUS HUMMINGBIRD
Selasphorus rufus

The Rufous Hummingbird is an inhabitant of the outskirts of forests from northwestern California to Alaska. It also visits parks and gardens to feed on flowering plants. These hummingbirds are about 9 cm long. The female builds her nest on

Rufous Hummingbird

Pileated Woodpecker

a branch, using plant material and strengthening the walls with spiders' webs. It is in this nest, lined with soft down, that she lays her 2 eggs, and then incubates them herself. She also looks after the young on her own.

These birds live on the nectar of flowers and on small flies and spiders. In late summer they leave their home and fly south to Mexico, where they spend the winter.

PILEATED WOODPECKER
Dryocopus pileatus

The Pileated Woodpecker lives in the great forests of southern Canada and the eastern half of the United States, though during the winter months it visits parks and orchards. It is a powerful bird, some 45 cm long. It feeds on insects and their larvae, seeds, nuts, berries and fruit. When spring comes, each pair of Pileated Woodpeckers works together to chip out a hole up to 1 m deep in the trunk of a large tree, and the female then lays 3—5 eggs. Both parents take turns to incubate the clutch, and later feed the young on ants and the larvae of wood beetles.

REPTILES

EASTERN CORAL SNAKE
Micrurus fulvius

The Eastern Coral Snake is found in the south-east of the United States and in northern Mexico, and is one of the most poisonous of the reptiles. During the day this brightly coloured snake, up to 100 cm in length, shelters beneath the loosened bark of a tree-stump or under flat stones. After dark it crawls into crevices in search of small lizards and snakes. It kills its victims

Eastern Coral Snake

with a bite from its poisonous fangs, then swallows them whole, head first.

The female lays 6—10 eggs in a damp hole in the ground. The young hatch about 3 months later, and are about 5 cm long.

INVERTEBRATES

BOLAS SPIDER
Mastophora bisaccata

The Bolas Spider occurs on the outskirts of forests, in parks and in gardens in the south-eastern United States. The female measures about 14 mm, the male 8 mm. It does not spin a web, but produces a special fibre, rather like a fishing line. On the end of this there is a small sticky ball. The spider holds this weighted thread with one of its front legs, and swings it round in a circle at high speed when a butterfly or moth is nearby. If it makes contact with the insect, the wings become firmly attached to the sticky blob, and the victim is hauled up. Then the spider takes hold of its prey with its front legs, bites it to death, winds fine fibres around it and eats it.

POLYPHEMUS MOTH
Antheraea polyphemus

The beautiful Polyphemus Moth is distributed from south-east Canada, through the eastern half of the United States to north-

Bolas Spider

Polyphemus Moth

eastern Mexico. It has a wingspan of 8.5—14 cm. These moths are mainly found in deciduous forests, and the female lays her eggs on various broad-leaved trees, particularly the oak, elm, white walnut and maple. When the caterpillars hatch, they feed on the leaves of the tree on which they were born. When they have matured they climb down to the ground, spin themselves a cocoon and pupate.

LUNA or AMERICAN MOON MOTH
Actias luna

The Luna, or American Moon Moth, is a beautiful moth with a wingspan of about 10 cm. It is found in the whole of the eastern half of the United States and in neighbouring parts of Canada, living in sparse woodland or the edges of deciduous forests.

Luna or American Moon Moth

The female lays her eggs mainly on walnut, maple and other deciduous trees, and the caterpillars pupate at the foot of the tree, on bark, or sometimes in the ground.

Photograph by Milan Holeček

Semidesert in Oaxaco state, Mexico

THE PRAIRIES, MOUNTAINS AND DESERTS OF NORTH AMERICA

COMMON or STRIPED SKUNK
Mephitis mephitis

The Common or Striped Skunk is one the best-known animals of North America. It is a carnivore, and reaches a length of 100 cm, including its tail. It lives on the outskirts of forests or on bushy prairies. During the day it hides in its den in a rocky crevice, a hollow stump or a hole beneath the roots of a bush or tree. After dark it pores over every crack and crevice of its territory. It attacks small mammals, catches small lizards and snakes, and eats insects and molluscs. From time to time it also eats fallen juicy fruit or berries. When threatened by a coyote or other enemy, a skunk sprays its adversary with a foul-smelling, yellowish fluid from glands beneath its tail.
The female gives birth to 3—8 young in her den.

COYOTE
Canis latrans

Coyotes are one of the best-known animals of the North American prairies. They are found from Alaska to Costa Rica and live in family groups, forming large packs in winter. They go hunting after sunset, and eat meat from the carcasses of large animals as well as rabbits, hares, rodents, birds, lizards and snakes. They collect dead fish, molluscs and other animals thrown up by the tide on the seashore, and in southern regions they dig up turtle eggs and steal poultry. They also take fruit from plantations.
The female gives birth to 3—4 pups in her den. During the first few days she does not leave her young for a moment, and is fed by her mate.

Common or Striped Skunk

Coyote

164

PUMA or MOUNTAIN LION
Felis concolor

The Puma, or Mountain Lion, is a powerful feline carnivore, up to 2.5 m long and weighing as much as 100 kg. It occurs throughout North, Central and South America, and is known by various names such as silver lion, cougar and panther. The Puma is mainly found in rocky areas and sparse forests, especially in the mountains. It likes to lie in wait for its prey in a tree or on a rocky ledge, from where it has a good view of tracks used by game. The Puma pounces on its unsuspecting victim from above and rarely misses its target. It preys mostly on various species of deer, and also catches hares, rabbits, rodents and birds.

During the mating season Pumas give out long, screeching calls; then after three months of pregnancy the female gives birth to 1—5 cubs in a cave.

AMERICAN BISON
Bison bison

The American Bison is one of the legends of the North American prairies. There were times when herds of millions of these animals wandered the countryside in search of food, followed by wolves, coyotes and nomadic Indian tribes, all of whom were able to live off the meat of the bison without endangering the numbers of these huge herds. The beasts of prey killed the weak and sickly Bison, helping to preserve the health of the herd. But then the white hunters came on the scene with their modern weapons, and in a short time almost wiped out the species. This destroyed the balance of nature over a wide area and also threatened the livelihood of the local Indians, whom the Bison provided with food and materials for making tents and clothes.

A bull Bison is 190 cm tall at the shoulders

Puma or Mountain Lion

American Bison

and may weigh more than 1 tonne, though cows are naturally smaller. Herds of Bison graze on grass and herbs, and in winter they dig in the snow for mosses and lichens.

Bison cows usually have 1 or occasionally 2 calves, which remain with their mother until the following winter.

ROCKY MOUNTAIN GOAT
Oreamnos americanus

The Rocky Mountain Goat is an inhabitant of mountain regions from south-west Alaska, through western Canada to Montana. The male reaches a height at the shoulder of about 100 cm, the female being smaller. They are found on the edges of the snowcap at a height of around 4 000 m above sea level, though in the winter they descend to lower levels. From spring to autumn they eat grass and the leaves and twigs of shrubs; in winter their diet is mainly mosses and lichens.

BIGHORN SHEEP
Ovis canadensis

The Bighorn Sheep is found in the rocky mountain ranges of western parts of the United States and south-west Canada. The male stands 100 cm tall at the shoulders,

Rocky Mountain Goat

Bighorn Sheep

weighs over 150 kg and has horns 70 cm long. The female is smaller with shorter, thinner horns, which are only slightly curved. The Bighorn Sheep climbs deftly up steep slopes and rocky hillsides, living on grass and the leaves and twigs of bushes. The sheep form small herds of 6—12, led by a strong ram.

PRONGHORN ANTELOPE
Antilocapra americana

The Pronghorn Antelope, a close relative of the sheep, is found in the prairies of the western and central United States, southern Canada and northern Mexico, but in many places it has died out. It is 90 cm tall at the shoulders, weighs 55 kg and is usually found in small groups led by a male. During the summer they roam in search of food, joining up into larger herds in winter. They eat grass, plants and the leaves of bushes. When threatened by danger, such as a wolf, the herd stampedes. They can run at a speed of 80 km per hour, and are the fastest land animals apart from cheetahs.

The female gives birth to twins, who follow her the day after they are born.

Pronghorn Antelope

167

BIRDS

CALIFORNIAN CONDOR
Gymnogyps californianus

The Californian Condor nests only in a small area along the coast of California. It is a huge bird of prey, 125 cm long with a wingspan of over 3 m. It is found among cliffs, from where it makes reconnaissance flights over mountain ravines or river banks in search of the carcasses of large animals.

Pairs of these condors make their nests in small caves in high cliffs. Usually in January or February, the female lays 1 or, rarely, 2 eggs. Both parents incubate the clutch, then the young condors take half a year to learn to fly.

SAGE GROUSE
Centrocercus urophasianus

The home of the Sage Grouse is the north-western United States. The male grows to a length of 70 cm and the female to 55 cm, and their habitat is bush-covered areas. In spring the cock birds gather in an open space and perform their courting ritual — they stick their tail feathers straight up in the air, puff out their chests, and inflate their red throat sacs like balloons. After this display the victorious male leads off about 75 per cent of the hen birds, the other males sharing the remaining females between them. The males take no part in nesting: females hollow out a shallow depression beneath a bush, lining it with grass and dry

Californian Condor

Sage Grouse

leaves. Here they lay 6—8 eggs. The mother also takes sole charge of the chicks, leading them about and protecting them. Sage Grouse live on insects, seeds, berries and green parts of plants.

BURROWING OWL
Speotyto cunicularia

The small Burrowing Owl is only about 23 cm long, with a wingspan of 55 cm. It is an inhabitant of prairies and semideserts from south-west Canada through the western half of the United States to South America. In southern regions it is resident, but in the north it migrates to the tropics in the autumn. Burrowing Owls find themselves the abandoned burrows of mammals, where they live and make their nests. On a lining of grass the female lays 2—12 eggs. Both parent birds take turns to incubate them, and both look after the young, feeding them on beetles, small rodents and occasional birds or frogs.

ROADRUNNER
Geococcyx californianus

The Roadrunner lives in deserts and semi-deserts from the south-west United States to central Mexico. It is an interesting bird, 60 cm long, half of which is its tail. It lives mainly on the ground, running rapidly over the sands with their thin cover of grass in search of its prey. Roadrunners hunt insects, small birds and rodents, and particularly like small snakes, often attacking even highly poisonous rattlesnakes. The Roadrunner seizes a snake or iguana behind the neck with its long, sharp beak, then smashes it several times violently against a flat stone to kill it before swallowing it head first. It also

Burrowing Owl

breaks open hard snail shells on stones and then swallows the soft mollusc bodies.

In April or May the birds build their nest of twigs in a low bush, lining it with sloughed snake skins. The female lays 4—10 eggs, and incubates them herself. The adults at first feed their young on insects, later on small vertebrates.

Roadrunner

169

REPTILES

GILA MONSTER
Heloderma suspectum

The Gila Monster, up to 60 cm long, is a venomous lizard which lives in dry areas of Utah, Nevada, Arizona and northern Mexico. During the day it shelters in holes which it digs beneath bushes, then after nightfall it slowly patrols its territory in search of something to eat. Gila Monsters eat insects, worms and small vertebrates, but their favourite foods are the eggs of birds and reptiles.

At the end of June the female buries 3—15 eggs in the sand, and the young hatch out after 30 days.

EASTERN DIAMOND-BACKED RATTLESNAKE
Crotalus adamanteus

The Eastern Diamond-backed Rattlesnake is one of the most venomous snakes, which lives in coastal regions in the south-east of North America. It is up to 2.5 m long and reaches a weight of 10 kg. These snakes are usually found in dry, bushy places. They are nocturnal, leaving their shelters after sunset to hunt small rodents and wild rabbits. If threatened or caught unawares, they roll into a ball and make a rattling noise with the tips of their tails to scare off any enemies.

In August or September the female usually has 8—12 live young.

Gila Monster

INVERTEBRATES

BLACK WIDOW SPIDER
Latrodectus mactans

The Black Widow Spider is the plague of the American countryside, although it is only small. The female measures about 15 mm, the male only about 5 mm. The venom of the female spider is very powerful and is fatal in 4.3 per cent of cases (10 per cent in the tropics), though she only bites when she is touched. Black Widow Spiders are found from southern Canada to the very tip of Tierra del Fuego. They live on the outskirts of forests, in bushes and outhouses, and even in occupied rooms or among clothes in people's wardrobes.

The female weaves a strong web, where the

Eastern Diamond-backed Rattlesnake

Black Widow Spider

Cicada Killer

Monarch

male goes to court her. After mating they part again. The female is likely to attack and eat her mate, thus becoming a widow, which accounts for her name. She lays her eggs in a special sac or cocoon, hung on a strong web and camouflaged with pieces of bark. Females eat insects, while the male eats nothing at all during his short life.

CICADA KILLER
Sphecius speciosus

The Cicada Killer, around 40 mm in length, lives in warm, sandy areas of North America. It digs out underground passages with a small chamber at the end, then it sets out to hunt large cicadas. It paralyzes its victims with its sting and drags them off to its home. When its chamber is full of cicadas, the female lays an egg on them, and once the larva has hatched it feeds off the food supply its mother has prepared for it. After having eaten the cicadas it pupates, and in a few weeks an adult insect emerges.

MONARCH
Danaus plexippus

The Monarch, a beautiful butterfly with a wingspan of 90 mm, occurs from southern Canada through the United States to South America. It migrates regularly from northern regions to the south, and huge flocks can be seen resting on the trees along the way in autumn. The female lays its eggs on milk weeds and periwinkles, and the caterpillars feed on the poisonous leaves of these plants. The poison does not harm them, but is stored in their bodies and passed on to the butterflies, so both can poison other animals. A bird which eats a Monarch caterpillar suffers cramps caused by the toxic glycosides, so if it recovers it is unlikely ever to attack this kind of caterpillar again.

Photograph by Oldřich Mazůrek

Canada, waterfalls in Ontario

THE
WATERS
AND
SWAMPS
OF
NORTH
AMERICA

MAMMALS

AMERICAN MINK
Mustela vison

The American Mink is distributed throughout almost all North America. Its usual habitat is close to rivers, streams or lakes, where it catches fish, amphibians and small mammals. Its favourite prey is the muskrat, and it also hunts small water birds and nestlings. Mink usually set out in search of food after dark, sheltering during the day in burrows dug out of the bank, where the female gives birth to 1—10 young.

The American Mink, which is about 50 cm long and 1 kg in weight, is widely bred on farms for its valuable fur.

CANADIAN OTTER
Lutra canadensis

The Canadian Otter lives in clear lakes and large rivers with unpolluted water throughout North America. This aquatic carnivore, up to 130 cm long and 15 kg in weight, dives beneath the water to hunt fish, muskrats, frogs, molluscs and insects. It digs its burrow in banks which are thickly overgrown with vegetation, building the entrance under water, so its home is perfectly hidden from its enemies. In a dry chamber lined with soft leaves and grass, the female gives birth in late spring to 2—4 young.

CANADIAN BEAVER
Castor canadensis

The Canadian Beaver is a strongly-built rodent, weighing up to 30 kg and about 100 cm long. It is found throughout almost the whole of North America, where it makes its home on streams and lakes. In running water the beaver builds itself extensive, elaborate dams about 120 cm wide and 50 cm high, constructed of branches weighted down with small stones. This produces a broad pool deep enough not to freeze over

American Mink

Canadian Otter

Canadian Beaver

Muskrat

in winter. Beavers keep a food supply of poplar and other twigs beneath the water to see them through the winter.

They also build burrows in banks at the waterside, with several underwater tunnels leading to their living area. In still water beavers build constructions called lodges made of branches, reeds and mud, and they line their lairs with grass and wood chips. They live mainly on the fresh bark of trees, and frequently fell trunks measuring up to 70 cm in diameter. They are particularly fond of poplars and birches, gnawing away the bark completely with their chisel-like teeth.

In a softly-lined lair the female gives birth to 2—6 young, which are born with a covering of hair and their eyes open.

MUSKRAT
Ondatra zibethica

The Muskrat is found in the rivers, lakes and pools of North America. It grows to a length of up to 60 cm, of which about 25 cm is its tail, and it weighs 1.5 kg. Muskrats live on leaves, shoots, roots, molluscs, crustaceans and fish. They dig out burrows several metres long in the banks of their home waters, or build lodges which are made up of heaps of aquatic plants up to 1 m high. In this den the female gives birth to 5—14 young, and older females may produce 4 litters a year.

The Muskrat has been introduced to Europe, where it spread rapidly and has bred in large numbers in some places.

AMERICAN or WHOOPING CRANE
Grus americana

The American or Whooping Crane was common in broad marshland areas from central Canada southwards to Iowa and Illinois. It has a wingspan of 225 cm and is 125 cm long. The cranes used to migrate in their thousands across the whole of the North American continent to winter in the vicinity of the Gulf of Mexico, and their clear cries could be heard as they flew overhead. But new settlers reclaimed the swamps where the cranes nested, and hunters shot them on a huge scale. Today these cranes nest only in the Canadian province of Saskatchewan, where there are a few dozen strictly protected pairs. In a jungle of reeds the birds build their large nests of sticks and reed stalks on small islands. The female lays 2 eggs and shares their incubation with her mate. The day after hatching the young cranes move about and even swim, though for the first few days their parents feed them on regurgitated food. Whooping Cranes live on insects, frogs, small mammals, seeds, berries and green parts of plants.

BALD EAGLE
Haliaeetus leucocephalus

The Bald Eagle, a huge bird of prey with a wingspan of 220 cm and weighing 6.5 kg, lives on the shores of large lakes and rivers and on the coast from Alaska to Florida. Adult birds live in pairs throughout their lives. In spring, when courting, Bald Eagles circle over their territories and their clear calls can often be heard. Pairs of these eagles usually build their nest of branches, lined with pine needles and grass, in tall trees. The female lays 2 or 3 eggs, which both parents incubate. The young stay in the nest for 10—11 weeks, and the adults feed them constantly. The main food of the Bald Eagle is fish, but it also hunts small

Bald Eagle

Trumpeter Swan

American or Whooping Crane

CANADA GOOSE
Branta canadensis

birds and mammals, and eats carrion floating on the surface of the water.

The Canada Goose, weighing up to 5 kg, is common from Alaska to the northern parts of the United States. In the nesting season

TRUMPETER SWAN
Cygnus buccinator

Canada Goose

The Trumpeter Swan weighs up to 13 kg and has a wingspan of 250 cm. Its home is in the northern lakes of North America, and it was once very abundant, but has now been almost eliminated by hunting.

In April the birds build a large nest of plants. There the female lays 3—5 eggs, which she surrounds with down and incubates herself. When the chicks have hatched, the parents immediately lead them to the water. Trumpeter Swans feed on aquatic and land plants, seeds, berries and small invertebrates.

Wood Duck

pairs of these birds are found beside large lakes or rivers. They build their nests, lined with dry leaves and blades of grass, on islands or in marshes, and the female lays 5—6 eggs, which she incubates herself. During this time her mate keeps watch nearby and drives off intruders. When the young are ready to leave the nest the families join up in flocks, which migrate south to winter on the coasts of the United States and Mex-ico. Canada Geese eat grass, grain, seeds, shoots, berries and sometimes insects and molluscs.

Canada Geese have also been introduced in the wild in Europe.

WOOD DUCK
Aix sponsa

The Wood Duck is mainly found in the eastern half of the United States, and also in the north-west. The courting plumage of the drake is the most colourful of any species of duck. However, from the end of May the males moult into a dull-coloured plumage similar to that of the females, regaining their bright colours in October. This small duck, about 50 cm long, lives on lakes and rivers with wooded banks. It builds its nest in a hole in a tree left by woodpeckers. The female lays 8—12 eggs, which she incubates herself for about 30 days. As soon as the ducklings have hatched and dried off, they jump out of the hole and drop to the ground, their fall broken by their own down. Then the mother leads them to the water. Wood Ducks live on seeds, berries, parts of plants, insects, molluscs, crustaceans and worms.

REPTILES

AMERICAN ALLIGATOR
Alligator mississippiensis

The American Alligator inhabits the south-eastern United States. It may reach a length of up to 6 m, but such large specimens are very rare and these alligators are usually 4 m long. They live mainly on fish, also catching amphibians, other reptiles, or birds and small mammals. The female builds herself a pile of leaves and clay up to 1 m high and 2 m across, where she lays 20—70 eggs. Then she stays nearby to keep watch. The young begin to hatch after 9—10 weeks,

178

American Alligator

and when the mother hears their cries she pushes away the top of the nest to help them get out. On hatching the young alligators are about 25 cm long, and are able to fend for themselves immediately, eating insects, their larvae and spiders.

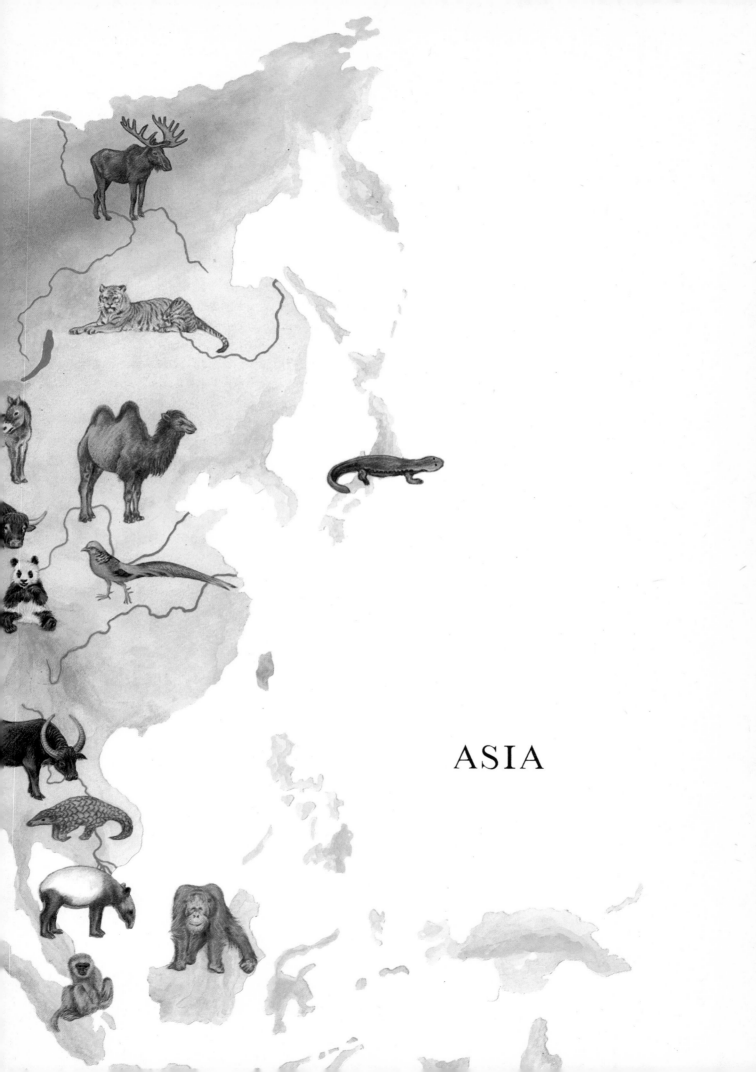

ASIA

Asia is the largest of the continents, forming a single landmass with Europe. Except for the Ural Mountains, there are no outstanding natural barriers between the two continents. There are many large islands off the coast of Asia, such as Sakhalin, the Japanese islands, Taiwan, the Philippines, the Indonesian Archipelago and Sri Lanka.

In the north of Asia there is a very cold, arctic climate, while in the south tropical conditions prevail. The differences in elevation (heights above sea level) in this continent are the greatest in the world. While Lake Baikal in the USSR is the world's deepest lake, the Himalayas, reaching a height of over 8 000 m, are the highest mountains on Earth.

All the different zones of vegetation are represented on the Asian continent, from the tundra in the far north, through the taiga (coniferous evergreen forests) and the central Asian plains and deserts, down to the tropical monsoon belt in the south, where regular rainy seasons alternate with long periods of drought. Each of these zones has its corresponding species of plants and animals.

Though there are huge, uninhabited areas in Asia—deserts, tundras, mountains and jungles—it is the home of more than half the world's entire population. The main population centres are on river deltas, in fertile valleys and along the sea coasts. Among the most heavily-populated areas are Japan, eastern China, Java in Indonesia, Bengal and some parts of southern and central India.

Asia has provided human beings with many livestock animals and crop plants without which life today would be difficult to imagine. It was in Asia, in today's Turkmenistan and Uzbekistan in the USSR, that the ancient bison which was the ancestor of our domestic cattle was first domesticated. The domestic buffalo, whose wild ancestor is still alive today, became an indispensable domestic animal throughout south and south-east Asia. In mountain regions the yak was domesticated. In the plains of Asia there once galloped great herds of Przewalski's horses, one of the forerunners of our modern horse, and now extremely rare in the wild. The Asian bezoar goat is an ancestor of the domestic goat, and the domestic sheep comes from western Asia. The most important of domestic birds, the hen, also has an Asian ancestor, the red jungle fowl. The silkworm, from eastern Asia, provides the valuable fibre from which silk is made. The native inhabitants of Asia also use a number of tamed wild animals, such as the elephant or the camel, or the reindeer in the far north, for heavy work.

The Tropical Rainforests of Asia

The whole of south and south-east Asia is covered with huge tropical rainforests. They are mostly deciduous, with many species of trees and shrubs. The most important of these to human beings are the trees which provide valuable timber for use in the manufacture of ships and many other things. Among the many highly-prized Asian woods is ebony, and palms are another important type of tree in tropical areas of the continent. They provide not only fruit, but also timber and huge leaves for use as a roof-covering.

Lianas are a typical feature of the rainforests. They are often tens of metres long, and are exceptionally strong, being used by the natives as ropes. The most important bushes of Asian origin are those of the genus *Citrus,* yielding tasty fruit. They are now cultivated in tropical and semitropical regions the world over. The banana is also grown on plantations throughout the tropics, and another very important Asian plant is the bamboo, which grows to a height of around 50 m. It has a wide variety of uses, from a food to the material for making rafts, huts, or even water-pipes. In the Indonesian region there are fascinating carnivorous plants which catch small insects, using them to provide nitrogen.

Photograph by Oldřich Mazůrek

Mountains and Rocky Areas

The Asian continent contains the most extensive and highest mountain ranges in the world. It is bordered to the west by the majestic Caucasus and the massive Urals, and eastwards from the Caucasus stretches the Iranian Plateau. This joins up with the Hindu Kush (which means 'murderers of Indians'). Particularly in the winter months, the Hindu Kush is notorious for its harsh weather, with frequent avalanches thundering down its precipitous slopes. Northwards stretch the famous Pamir range, known as the 'Roof of the World', and the Tien Shan, China's 'Heavenly Mountains'.

In central Asia the Altai Mountains soar up from the surrounding countryside, and eastwards from the Pamir stretch the Karakoram Range and the Tibetan Plateau. The southern part of this gigantic range is formed by the towering Himalayas, including the world's highest mountain, Mount Everest, which is over 8 800 m high.

From the foothills to the snowline, the mountains of Asia teem with life, and in spring countless species of plants and bushes burst into flower on the mountain slopes providing anyone lucky enough to see them with a colourful sight.

Photograph by Ivo Petřík

Deserts and Plains

Inland, in central Asia, there are huge areas of desert. The biggest of these is the Gobi Desert, but the Karakum, Takla Makan and Saudi Arabian Rub'al Khali are also very large. The Thar Desert in north-west India is another well-known desert region. Some of these deserts are sandy, while others are stony, but all of them support life. In places there are patches of grass or bushes, while elsewhere the desert surface is covered with salt, providing a home for the small desert plants which tolerate salt.

Perhaps the most typical plants of the Asian deserts are the low, prickly bushes of the genus *Alhagi,* whose thorn-protected leaves are eaten only by camels and sheep. Green plants are to be found in the desert only in the short spring season, and in summer all plants are parched and scorched by the wind and sun. The temperature in the shade often rises to as much as 50° C, and the surface of the desert is baked until it resembles hot ash.

The Asian plains are notable for their highly-scented wormwood plants, while in damp valleys tamarisks and mulberry trees thrive. Sugar cane has spread to tropical regions throughout the world from Bengal in India, and Assam was the original home of the tea plant.

Photograph by Ivo Petřík

Waters and Swamps

The glaciers of the Himalayas, Tibet and other huge Asian mountain ranges feed most of the continent's great rivers. In spring, when the ice begins to melt, river levels rise sharply. In southern Asia, summer brings the heavy monsoon rains when the rivers rise above their banks, flooding vast lowland areas. In these regions the annual floods cause immense damage. Rivers such as the sacred Ganges often cut deep new channels. The floodwaters of the River Indus also cover villages and towns, and regularly fill the swamps which are found in a wide surrounding area. The longest river in Asia is China's Yangtze Kiang, which rises in Tibet.

The coastal areas of the Asian tropics, and the deltas of the huge rivers of south and south-east Asia, have a character all their own. Thick growths of several species of mangrove trees and bushes form an impenetrable, permanently green thicket. In places various species of tall, slender palm trees line the shore. Most of them are invaluable to the natives. The fronds of some species make an excellent roof-covering for wooden huts, and their flowers are used to make wine. Palm-fronds of the genus *Pandasus* are used for making strong mats, hats, and even sails for boats.

Of all the tropical palms of Asia the most famous is the coconut palm, which originated on the coral islands of Polynesia. It grows to over 20 m tall, and is of immense importance to the native population. The trunks are used to make furniture, the broad leaves for matting and roofing, and the unripe flowers yield syrup used in the production of sugar. But most important of all are the coconuts themselves, which provide coconut milk; the dried pulp (called copra) is pressed to obtain oil, and desiccated coconut is used in cooking. In addition, the fibres around the shell are used in the textile industry in home and factory-made carpets, matting, brushes, and many other useful items. The coconut industry of tropical Asia is therefore of vital importance.

Photograph by Oldřich Mazůrek

ASIA

MAMMALS

Argali

Babirusa
Bear, Asiatic Black or Moon
Bear, Malayan Sun
Binturong
Blackbuck
Bobak
Buffalo, Water
Bull, Blue or Nilgai

Camel, Bactrian
Chital or Axis Deer
Civet, Masked Palm

Deer, Axis or Chital
Desman, Russian
Dhole or Asiatic Red Wolf

Elephant, Indian

Fox, Indian Flying

Gibbon, White-handed or Lar
Goat, Wild
Goral

Hamster, Golden
Hedgehog, Long-eared
Horse, Przewalski's

Langur, Douc
Langur, Entellus
Lemur, Philippine Flying
Leopard, Clouded
Leopard, Snow or Ounce
Loris, Slender
Loris, Slow

Macaque, Stump-tailed
Markhor
Mongoose, Common or Newara
Monkey, Proboscis
Monkey, Rhesus

Muntjac, Indian

Newara or Common Mongoose
Nilgai or Blue Bull

Onager, Persian
Orang-utan
Ounce or Snow Leopard

Panda, Giant
Panda, Lesser
Pika, Steppe

Rhinoceros, Indian One-horned

Saiga
Sambar
Shrew, Common Tree
Siamang
Squirrel, Oriental Giant

Tapir, Malayan
Tarsier, Western
Tiger, Bengal

Wolf, Asiatic Red or Dhole

Yak, Wild

BIRDS

Bee-eater, Blue-cheeked

Cockatoo, Salmon-crested or
    Pink-crested
Crane, Demoiselle

Dove, Rock

Eagle, Philippine Monkey-eating
Eagle, Tawny

Fowl, Red Jungle

Hornbill, Great Pied

Jacana, Pheasant-tailed

Kingfisher, White-breasted
Kite, Black

Lammergeier or Bearded Vulture

Magpie, Green
Mynah, Hill

Owl, Malaysian Fish

Parakeet, Bearded or Red-breasted
Peafowl, Common
Pheasant, Crimson Horned or Satyr
    Tragopan
Pheasant, Golden
Pheasant, Himalayan Monal
Pheasant, Lady Amherst's
Pheasant, Reeve's
Pheasant, Ring-necked
Pigeon, Luzon Bleeding-heart

Starling, Rose Coloured
Stork, Black-necked

Tragopan, Satyr or Crimson Horned
    Pheasant

Vulture, Asian King
Vulture, Bearded or Lammergeier
Vulture, Black

REPTILES

Alligator, Chinese

Cobra, Indian
Cobra, King or Hamadryad

Gavial, Indian
Gecko Teratoscincus scincus

Hamadryad or King Cobra

Lizard, Common Flying

Python, Reticulated

Tokay
Tortoise, Four-toed

Viper, Russell's

AMPHIBIANS

Salamander, Giant

INVERTEBRATES

Butterfly, Common Map
Butterfly, Indian Leaf

Moon-moth, Indian
Moth Erasmia sanguiflua
Moth, Owl
Moving Leaf

Stick Insect

THE TROPICAL RAINFORESTS OF ASIA

Nepal — lush tropical vegetation predominates in mountain valleys

MAMMALS

PHILIPPINE FLYING LEMUR
Cynocephalus volans

The Philippine Flying Lemur is an inhabitant of the tropical rainforests of the Philippines. It grows to a length of 70 cm, though about 25 cm of this is tail. During the daytime it sleeps, hanging from a branch, then after dark it crawls along branches, still hanging upside down, or moves along tree trunks in short leaps. Sometimes it hurls itself from a branch, spreading the broad fold of skin between its fore and hind legs and gliding to a distance of up to 140 m. It lives exclusively on the leaves and shoots of eucalyptus trees.

Two months after mating the female gives birth, usually to a single offspring. At first she carries it with her everywhere, and it clings to her stomach.

INDIAN FLYING FOX
Pteropus giganteus

The Indian Flying Fox is found in Sri Lanka and India. It is about 30 cm long, and the span of its webbed wings is more than 120 cm. These are gregarious animals, living in groups of hundreds or thousands. During the day Flying Foxes rest, hanging upside down from their regular perches in huge trees. As soon as night begins to fall they wake up, start to climb, and screech noisily. Suddenly, the whole enormous pack takes off, flying like a black cloud to seek ripe, juicy fruit in the forest.

After a period of 180 days females give birth to a single young, which for the first 4 months clings tightly to its mother's fur with its sharp claws.

COMMON TREE SHREW
Tupaia glis

The Common Tree Shrew lives in the tropical forests of Asia. It reaches a length of 40 cm, though more than half of this is taken up by its tail. It moves nimbly along branches, confidently leaping from tree to tree. It usually makes its lair in a hole left by woodpeckers, and here the female gives birth to twins. The Common Tree Shrew

Philippine Flying Lemur

Indian Flying Fox

Common Tree Shrew

Slender Loris

mostly eats insects, as well as catching the young of small vertebrates and taking birds' eggs. It is also fond of ripe, sweet fruit.

SLENDER LORIS
Loris tardigradus

The Slender Loris is a primate about 25 cm long, with a short tail. It lives in trees in the tropical forests of southern India and Sri Lanka. In the daytime it sleeps on a branch, rolled up in a ball, then after sunset it crawls slowly and carefully around the crowns of trees, looking for insects. If it comes across a bird's nest it will eat the eggs or young, and another favourite food is ripe, juicy fruit or berries.

In a hole in a tree, lined with soft leaves, the female gives birth to a single young.

SLOW LORIS
Nycticebus coucang

The Slow Loris is found across south-east Asia from Assam to Indonesia. It is a short-tailed primate which grows to a length of

40 cm and weighs up to 1.5 kg. In the day-time it sleeps in the hollow of a tree, then as soon as darkness falls it leaves its shelter and climbs slowly along the branches within its territory. It hunts insects and small lizards, and also likes the eggs and young of birds, bamboo shoots and sweet fruit.

A single young is born to the female in a tree hollow after a gestation period 185 days.

WESTERN TARSIER
Tarsius bancanus

The tropical forests of the large Indonesian islands of Sumatra, Kalimantan (Borneo) and Sulawesi (Celebes) are the home of the strange nocturnal primate, the Western Tarsier. It has eyes as big as an owl's and fingers spread out at the ends like a huge frog's. The Tarsier's body is 12—14 cm long; its 20-cm-long tail is used as a rudder when jumping from branch to branch. During the day it sleeps in the treetops, then during its nightly foraging trips it mostly catches insects and their larvae.

Slow Loris

Western Tarsier

The female gives birth to a single offspring, which is suckled for half a year.

RHESUS MONKEY
Macaca mulatta

The Rhesus Monkey is a member of the large group of monkeys called macaques. As a result of experiments in blood transfusion carried out on this monkey, scientists first discovered the so-called Rhesus factor, which is very important in medicine. Rhesus Monkeys are found through southern and south-eastern Asia, living in troops in thick vegetation along river banks or among tall bushes in rocky areas. The group is led by the strongest male. On their regular daily foraging expeditions the monkeys eat plant shoots, berries, fruit, seeds and nuts. They sleep in caves in steep cliffs or in the tree-tops.

The female usually has a single young, which she carries on her stomach.

PROBOSCIS MONKEY
Nasalis larvatus

The strange-looking Proboscis Monkey lives in the jungles of Kalimantan (Borneo). The male weighs over 20 kg, but the female is only half that size. Adult males have a huge nose, reaching down to their chins, which acts as a sort of amplifier and is used by the

Rhesus Monkey

193

Siamang

Proboscis Monkey

leader of the troop to announce his territory. Proboscis Monkeys eat young leaves, fruit and juicy water plants, which they gather by hanging from the trees on lianas. A young, inexperienced monkey may fall into the water, but they are good swimmers and easily get back on dry land.

The female has a single young, which she carries on her stomach.

SIAMANG
Symphalangus syndactylus

Few animals have a voice as powerful as that of the Siamang. It has a resonant pouch beneath its throat which amplifies its cries. Siamangs live in the mountainous forests of the Mentawai Islands, which are off the west coast of Sumatra. They are up

to 90 cm tall and weigh 8—11 kg, forming family groups and living mainly in the tops of tall trees. Their chief diet is fruit, but they also eat young, green shoots and occasional insects and they like birds' eggs.

The female has a single offspring, which clings to the hair on her chest.

WHITE-HANDED or LAR GIBBON
Hylobates lar

The White-handed or Lar Gibbon is found from south-east Asia to Sumatra. It lives in the rainforests up to a height of 2 400 m above sea-level, is about 60 cm long and weighs up to 8 kg. These gibbons live in family groups, and each has its own territory. They spend almost the whole of their lives in the treetops, where their usual way of moving around is hanging from the branches by their arms. They live on sweet, juicy fruit, leaves, insects, birds' eggs and small vertebrates.

194

The female has a single young, which clings tightly to the hair on her stomach.

ORANG-UTAN
Pongo pygmaeus

The Orang-utan's home is on the Indonesian islands of Sumatra and Kalimantan (Borneo), in rainforests and mountainous areas up to a height of 2 000 m. These are powerfully-built apes, an adult male weighing up to 100 kg, while the smaller female weighs only 50 kg. They live in pairs or in family groups with 1—3 young of various ages. They keep to the crowns of tall trees, where they also gather food — mainly various fruits, berries, nuts and shoots. When the weather is cold or wet they build a simple nest of branches, and sleep there covered with leaves.
The female Orang-utan has a single young, which at first clings tightly to its mother's stomach.

ORIENTAL GIANT SQUIRREL
Ratufa bicolor

The Oriental Giant Squirrel is a rodent which lives in the dense jungles of the whole of south-east Asia, from where it has spread northwards as far as Nepal. It grows to a length of 90 cm, more than half of which is its tail. Giant Squirrels are arboreal, rarely descending to the ground. They climb deftly among the branches in the treetops, gathering seeds, nuts, fruit, berries and shoots. They occasionally also catch insects, and sometimes take the young or eggs

Orang-utan

Oriental Giant Squirrel

from small birds' nests. At night they sleep in a large hole in a tree, where the female also gives birth to 2—3 young after a month-long gestation period.

MALAYAN SUN BEAR
Helarctos malayanus

The Malayan Sun Bear lives in the great jungles from southern China to Sumatra and Kalimantan (Borneo). It is the smallest of the bears, growing to a length of only 140 cm and weighing 27—65 kg. Most of the year it lives alone, pairing for a short time only at the mating season. After about 3 months the female then gives birth in a softly-lined den to a single young, rarely to twins.

This bear is active at night, sleeping by day in a nest of broken branches or basking in the sun on an exposed branch. It patrols a wide area around its home in search of food, and likes juicy fruit, which it climbs trees to pick or gathers on the ground. It sometimes goes into maize fields or banana plantations, looks for the nests of wild bees, and catches frogs, reptiles and small mammals from time to time.

BINTURONG
Arctictis binturong

The Binturong, a small civet-like carnivore, is found throughout south-east Asia. It lives in dense jungles, particularly in the mountains, and has very long fur which protects it from the cold night air. The Binturong is

Malayan Sun Bear

Binturong

Masked Palm Civet

about 180 cm long, half of which is its bushy tail. It sleeps in the hollow of a tree during the day, setting out after sunset to patrol its territory. It climbs deftly among the treetops, looking for birds' nests with eggs or young, and eating soft fruit or berries.

About 3 months after mating the female gives birth to 1 — 2 young inside her lair.

MASKED PALM CIVET
Paguma larvata

The home of the Masked Palm Civet is in south-east Asia, southern China and north-

ern India. It is a pretty carnivore, growing to a length of over 135 cm, of which about 60 cm is its tail. During the day it sleeps in a hole in a tree, setting out to feed after dark. It eats insects, frogs, tree geckos, the eggs and young from birds' nests and ripe fruit.

The female gives birth to 3 — 4 young in her lair.

CLOUDED LEOPARD
Neofelis nebulosa

The Clouded Leopard is one of the most beautiful of the Big Cats. It is found

Clouded Leopard

197

Bengal Tiger

throughout south-east Asia from southern China and eastern India to Sumatra and Kalimantan (Borneo). It is about 190 cm long, 90 cm of which is its tail. Clouded Leopards live in tropical forests and are solitary for most of the year—only in the mating season does the male find himself a mate, with whom he stays for a few days. After a gestation period of 3 months the female gives birth to 1—5 young in a den in a hollow tree or a cave. Clouded Leopards usually hunt by day, though sometimes also at night. They climb trees and catch mammals, especially monkeys, or birds.

BENGAL TIGER
Panthera tigris tigris

The Bengal Tiger is found in India and the north of south-east Asia. It is a massive member of the cat family, 100 cm tall at the shoulder, 350 cm long, including its tail, and about 180 kg in weight. Bengal Tigers are found in jungle forests in both highlands

and lowlands, and also in extensive reed beds in swampy areas and near rivers. Each tiger has its own large territory in which to hunt, and only in the mating season does the male find himself a mate, with whom he lives for a short time. In a sheltered place the tigress later gives birth to 1—6 cubs.

The tiger hunts its prey in daylight or at twilight, dragging it to the ground with its huge paws and biting into its neck. It then drags larger prey to a spot near water, where it can both eat and drink. It is very unusual for Bengal Tigers to become man-eaters, but those which do have to be hunted down and killed.

INDIAN ELEPHANT
Elephas maximus

South and south-east Asia is the home of one of the largest of all mammals, the Indian Elephant, which grows up to 3.1 m tall and may weigh over 5 tonnes. If the male has tusks they may be up to 160 cm long;

Babirusa

the female has none. Elephants are still used as working animals to carry heavy loads in India.

Elephants live in herds, wandering through the jungle, bamboo forests and swamps, each using its own regular tracks to go to and from water-holes. Elephants drink by sucking the water into their trunks, then squirting it into their mouths, and feed on grass, leaves, twigs and various fruit.

After a gestation period of 22 months the female gives birth to a calf weighing 50—120 kg, which follows its mother after only 2 days. Young elephants suck their mother's milk directly into their mouths for 8—10 months.

BABIRUSA
Babyrousa babyrussa

The Babirusa is a species of wild pig found on the island of Sulawesi (Celebes). It weighs up to 90 kg, and its habitat is in forests, thick bushes or reeds along river banks. Babirusas go out to feed after dark, eating leaves, shoots, various fruits and aquatic plants, for which they wade into shallow water. In loose soil they also grub up worms, molluscs or insect larvae.

In the mating season the usually solitary males find themselves females; after less than 5 months the mother gives birth to twins.

Indian Elephant

Indian Muntjac

feeding on grass, herbs, the leaves of bushes and fallen fruit.

The female usually has 1 or more rarely 2 offspring.

SAMBAR
Cervus unicolor

The Sambar is an inhabitant of the huge jungles of south and south-east Asia. It is a massive deer, up to 155 cm tall at the shoulder, and the males have powerful antlers with only a few tines. Sambars usually go out to graze in the daytime, eating grass, the twigs of bushes and trees, various fruits, bamboo shoots, lichen and moss.

About 9 months after mating the hind gives birth to a single young in a sheltered place in the thicket.

AXIS DEER or CHITAL
Axis axis

The Axis Deer, or Chital, 80 cm tall at the shoulder and weighing up to 45 kg, is a native of India and Sri Lanka. They live in large herds in thinly forested areas, usually near water, where they take refuge when in danger. They usually graze in the daytime.

About 7 months after mating hinds give birth to 1—2 or sometimes to 3 fawns.

NILGAI or BLUE BULL
Boselaphus tragocamelus

The Nilgai, or Blue Bull, inhabits the open plains of India. The male stands 150 cm tall and weighs 200 kg, with short antlers, and the smaller, brown female is hornless. Nilgai live in small groups, but old males are solitary outside the mating season. They eat grass, leaves and fruits.

The female usually gives birth to twins.

INDIAN MUNTJAC
Muntiacus muntjak

The Indian Muntjac, a small deer, occurs throughout south and south-east Asia as far as the island of Bali. It is only 50 cm tall at the shoulder and weighs 15—18 kg. The male has small antlers up to 15 cm long with a single tine; the female has none. The Muntjac lives in dense jungle vegetation and in inaccessible thickets along the banks of rivers. The animals make tunnel-like tracks through the undergrowth, which they mark with secretions exuded from a gland on the chin. They spend the whole night

Sambar

Nilgai or Blue Bull

Axis Deer or Chital

201

PHILIPPINE MONKEY-EATING EAGLE
Pithecophaga jefferyi

The Philippine Monkey-eating Eagle is a huge bird of prey with a wingspan of over 2 m which is found in the jungles of the Philippines. It is the terror of monkeys and other small animals, pursuing its chosen prey among the branches and homing in on its target like a guided missile.

Pairs of Monkey-eating Eagles build their nests in a huge tree, most often in *Sapium luzonicum.* They make a huge structure of branches, lined with green leaves, and the female sits on her single egg alone, while her mate supplies her with food. During the first few days the mother divides up the prey before feeding it to the eaglet.

RING-NECKED PHEASANT
Phasianus colchicus

The Ring-necked Pheasant is found from the Caucasus to east and south-east Asia, and has also been introduced in Europe and the United States. The highly colourful cock bird is up to 90 cm long, while the brown-coloured hen is about 60 cm. The Ring-necked Pheasant is found in thin woodland in uplands or mountains, never leaving its

Philippine Monkey-eating Eagle

Ring-necked Pheasant

native territory even in winter. It is not a good flier, being capable of rapid but not sustained flight, so after a steep take-off it soon glides down again. Each cock pheasant has a small territory of his own. He gathers around himself 3—5 hen birds, but after mating takes no further care of his family. Hens make a shallow nest in a clump of grass or at the foot of a tree which they line with dry leaves and grass; there they lay 8—15 eggs each and incubate them for 22—27 days. The mother takes her chicks with her to find food, and the young live on insects, spiders, molluscs, small leaves and grass. Adult birds also gather seeds and pick berries.

RED JUNGLE FOWL
Gallus gallus

The Red Jungle Fowl occurs in the jungles of south and south-east Asia, southern Sumatra, Java and Bali. The male, which has beautiful long tail feathers, measures 70 cm, and the female is 40 cm in length. During the mating season cock birds defend a terri-

tory, and each has 5—6 mates. In a nest on the ground the hen bird lays 5—7 eggs; she incubates these herself, and also looks after the young on her own. Red Jungle Fowl feed on seeds, berries, green shoots and invertebrates such as insects, spiders, worms and molluscs.

Red Jungle Fowl

Reeve's Pheasant

REEVE'S PHEASANT
Syrmaticus reevesii

The home of the Reeve's Pheasant is the sparse mountain forests of northern and central China. The cock bird, which has beautifully coloured plumage, grows to a length of up to 210 cm, but 180 cm of this consists of the long central tail feathers. An older cock mates with 2—3 hen birds, each of which lays 7—15 eggs. The females incubate these themselves, and also look after the young on their own. Reeve's Pheasants live on seeds, berries, grass, green leaves and invertebrates, especially insects and worms.

GOLDEN PHEASANT
Chrysolophus pictus

The Golden Pheasant is found in the mountain forests of central China. The magnificently coloured male is 110 cm long, including the 80-cm ornamental tail feathers. During the mating season the male has up to eight mates, each of which makes a shallow depression beneath a dense bush which she lines with leaves and blades of grass. She then lays 5—12 eggs, which she incubates herself. Golden Pheasants live on green shoots, seeds, spiders, insects, worms and molluscs.

The Red Jungle Fowl is an ancestor of the domestic hen. It is known that fowl were domesticated as early as 3 200 B.C. in India, for they are depicted in statues and paintings on pottery representing the Indian culture of that time.

Golden Pheasant

COMMON PEAFOWL
Pavo cristatus

The Common Peafowl is a native of the lowland and mountain regions of India and Sri Lanka, where it lives in the jungle in small groups. The peacock reaches a length of 220 cm, but over 150 cm of this consists of his tail. Males open out their beautiful tail feathers to form a huge coloured fan, which attracts the peahens during courtship. A cock bird normally lives with 4—5 hens, with which he goes out to feed. In a shallow depression scantily lined with leaves, the hen lays 4—8 eggs; these she incubates herself, and it is she who subsequently cares for the chicks. Peafowl eat insects and other invertebrates, and also small vertebrates, green shoots, seeds and berries.

LUZON BLEEDING-HEART PIGEON
Gallicolumba luzonica

The Luzon Bleeding-heart Pigeon is about 26 cm long and lives in the forests of the Philippine islands of Luzon and Polillo. These birds live in pairs when nesting, otherwise in family groups. They feed on the ground, beneath trees and bushes, where they eat seeds and berries, or occasional small insects, spiders and other invertebrates. Nesting pairs build on a branch, using twigs and dry grass stalks. The female lays 2 eggs, which she takes turns with her mate to incubate, and both parents also feed the young.

BEARDED or RED-BREASTED PARAKEET
Psittacula alexandri

The Bearded or Red-Breasted Parakeet is a 33-cm-long member of the parrot family.

Common Peafowl

Luzon Bleeding-heart Pigeon

Bearded or Red-breasted Parakeet

Salmon-crested or Pink-crested Cockatoo

It is a native of south-east Asia, southern China and the Himalayan region. In the nesting season it lives in pairs, afterwards flying about the dense forests in small flocks of up to 50 birds. In the tops of tall trees these parakeets search for seeds, soft fruit, berries and shoots, and they make their nests in tree hollows. The female lays 3—4 eggs, which she incubates herself, then both parents feed the young.

SALMON-CRESTED or PINK-CRESTED COCKATOO
Cacatua moluccensis

The Salmon-crested or Pink-crested Cockatoo grows to a length of more than 50 cm. It is found on the southern Moluccan islands of Seram, Saparua and Haruku, where it lives in huge forests, though it may sometimes also be seen in urban parks where large trees grow. In the treetops it looks for food — fruit, berries, nuts, seeds, leaves and fine bark. It can also shell nuts with its strong beak.

These cockatoos make their nests in large tree hollows. Here the female lays 2 eggs, which she takes turns with her mate to incubate, then both of them also feed the young.

GREAT PIED HORNBILL
Buceros bicornis

The Great Pied Hornbill is distributed from south-western China across Thailand and Sumatra, and is mostly found on thickly-wooded hills. These birds live in pairs or in family groups of 3—5 which sometimes

Great Pied Hornbill

Hill Mynah

merge to form flocks of over 30 birds. The Great Pied Hornbill eats figs, nutmegs, various berries and fallen fruit and is also fond of small rodents, lizards, snakes and nestlings.

Pairs of hornbills make their nests in holes in huge trees. When the female is ready to lay she goes into the nest, then blocks the entrance with a mixture of clay, sticky pieces of fig, droppings and leaves. She remains inside, with only a narrow crack through which to put her beak. In her voluntary prison she is well-protected from predators, and is regularly fed by her mate as she incubates 2 eggs. The male then also feeds the young. When these are 14 days old, the parents break open the wall and the female flies out. The adults then close up

the hole again and both continue to feed the chicks, which remain inside until they are fully fledged.

HILL MYNAH
Gracula religiosa

The Hill Mynah is found in forests throughout south and south-east Asia, and is 30 cm long. Outside the nesting season small groups of these birds fly about the tops of trees or among tall bushes, eating ripe berries and figs. They also eat seeds and nectar from trees, sometimes catching insects and small tree lizards.

Pairs of Hill Mynahs often stay together all their lives. They nest in hollows abandoned by woodpeckers and construct their nests from leaves, grass, moss and feathers. The female then lays 2—3 eggs, which she and the male take turns to incubate; both of them also feed the young.

207

Green Magpie

GREEN MAGPIE
Cissa chinensis

The brightly coloured Green Magpie occurs from the Himalayas and south-east Asia to Sumatra and Borneo. These birds are never still for a moment, constantly looking for nests from which to take eggs or young birds. They also hunt small arboreal lizards, frogs and insects.

Green Magpies build their nests of twigs, bamboo leaves, moss and roots, lining them with soft lichen. The female lays 3—5 eggs, which are incubated by both parents. Adult birds grow to 40 cm long.

REPTILES

COMMON FLYING LIZARD
Draco volans

The Common Flying Lizard is an inhabitant of Indonesia and the south of the Malayan peninsula, and is also known as the Flying Dragon. It is a small arboreal lizard, no more than 20 cm long, which has 5 or 6 pairs of long ribs growing out of each side of its body. Between these stretches a flexible membrane. When the lizard launches

Common Flying Lizard

King Cobra or Hamadryad

itself into the air, it spreads this membrane wide and can glide from tree to tree. The Flying Lizard lives on insects and their larvae, and on spiders. The female lays eggs with a leathery membrane, from which completely independent young emerge after a few weeks.

KING COBRA or HAMADRYAD
Ophiophagus hannah

The King Cobra, or Hamadryad, is the largest of the venomous snakes, reaching a length of up to 5.5 m. As a result of its size, the cobra can inject large doses of highly toxic venom. If no serum is available, a human victim dies within a few hours, and neck and head bites prove fatal within minutes. Even elephants have died after being bitten in the soft skin at the tip of their trunks. Fortunately, King Cobras are not aggressive, and try to frighten away their adversaries by rearing up the front of their bodies and spreading their hoods.

These snakes are distributed in the forests from eastern India, through south-east Asia, Indonesia and the Philippines. The female builds a two-storey domed nest in a heap of bamboo shoots and leaves, carrying the material in a coil at the front of her long body. In the bottom chamber of the nest she lays 30—40 eggs, while she lies in a coil, guarding the clutch, in the upper part. The male sometimes takes over guard duties. The young hatch after 3 months; they are independent at once, and are able to bite. King Cobras prey mainly on other snakes, both venomous and non-venomous, and on lizards.

STICK INSECT
Cyphocrania gigas

The Stick Insect *Cyphocrania gigas,* one of the largest species of its genus, reaches a length of about 25 cm. It inhabits the tropical zoné of southern Asia and is found in bushes and trees in thin woodland. It resembles a dry twig and this enables it to escape the attention of predators, although it is often captured by large insectivorous birds or lizards. This insect hatches from an egg and sheds its skin several times during

Indian Leaf Butterfly

Common Map Butterfly

Moth *Erasmia sanguiflua*

Moving Leaf

Stick Insect *Cyphocrania gigas*

its development, before reaching its final size.

MOVING LEAF
Phyllium siccifolium

The Moving Leaf is a leaf insect of southeast Asia and the adjacent islands. Its flattened legs and very broad, flat body make it look exactly like a green leaf. Indeed, many natives believe that these insects originated from leaves that grew legs. The female is about 10 cm long, while the male is smaller. Leaf insects usually sit motionless and invisible among the leaves on which they feed at night. When they are disturbed, they stand up on their thin legs and begin to swing. This often deters smaller insectivor-

ous birds. The female lays large greyish eggs, which resemble seeds. These insects moult several times before they are fully grown.

COMMON MAP BUTTERFLY
Cyrestis thyodamas

The Common Map Butterfly ranges from India to New Guinea. This large species has a wingspan averaging 65 mm. It rests with spread wings on the ground or on the bushes, choosing half-shaded places in the jungle. Here the map-like pattern on its wings makes it almost invisible. However, in flight it is frequently caught by insectivorous birds. This butterfly is often seen drinking from the edges of puddles or from dewdrops.

210

INDIAN LEAF BUTTERFLY
Kallima inachus

The Indian Leaf Butterfly inhabits forested areas of India and Sri Lanka. It has a wingspan of 85 mm, and, unusually for butterflies, it has projections on the tips of its forewings. These formations are of great importance. When the butterfly rests on a twig and folds its wings, the underside looks just like a large leaf, complete with central vein and stalk. This enables the butterfly to escape attention among the dense branches. When the butterfly is disturbed it quickly spreads its wings, revealing two eye-like spots which often scare away such predators as small birds or lizards.

MOTH
Erasmia sanguiflua

The Moth *Erasmia sanguiflua* is one of the largest and most colourful species of its genus. It has a wingspan of about 95 mm. During the day, it flies apparently hesitantly, over meadows or along the edges of forests, often alighting on tall plants. At night it shelters beneath large leaves. This beautiful moth is native to southern Asia.

OWL MOTH
Brahmaea wallichii

The Owl Moth has a characteristic, highly intricate and dense wing pattern, and its wingspan is in excess of 15 cm. It occurs in forested areas of tropical Asia, flying among the trees by night, and resting on them by day. The caterpillar has a bizarre appearance. It is yellowish-green and is patterned in black and yellow. In its first larval stages it has 4 outgrowths on the front part of the body and 2 on the hind part. These spines look like pieces of twisted wire and are shed during the last moult. Before pupation, the caterpillar turns a rich orange colour.

INDIAN MOON-MOTH
Actias selene

The Indian Moon-moth has a wingspan of up to 12 cm. It is distributed in forested areas from Japan to southern China, India and Sri Lanka. During the day it hides away among the large, dense leaves of trees and bushes, and at night it flies along the edges of jungles or in thin woodland. The female lays her eggs on the leaves of various trees, frequently walnuts.

Owl Moth

Indian Moon-moth

211

Photograph by Ivo Petřík

The Caucasus, Mt. Kazbek

MOUNTAINS
AND
ROCKY
AREAS

MAMMALS

DOUC LANGUR
Pygathrix nemaeus

The Douc Langur, a powerfully-built monkey, lives in rocky areas and jungles in Laos, Vietnam and the island of Hainan Dao. It is 150 cm long, half of which is its tail. Douc Langurs live in small family groups, consisting of several females with their young led by a single adult male. During the day the monkeys roam the edges of forests or the valleys of mountain streams, picking various fruits, flowers, shoots and young leaves of bushes and trees. They have no fixed territory, and the groups often meet during their forays.

The female gives birth to a single young, which clings tightly to the fur of its mother's stomach.

STUMP-TAILED MACAQUE
Macaca arctoides

The Stump-tailed Macaque is found in mountainous regions with wooded rocky slopes on the banks of streams in south-east Asia. This monkey is about 65 cm long with a short tail, and lives in troops led by the strongest of the males. During the day they climb about the bushes and low trees, foraging for shoots, leaves, fruit and berries. They sometimes catch insects and small vertebrates or take birds' eggs, and spend the night in caves, usually among rocks above a river.

Douc Langur

Stump-tailed Macaque

The female gives birth to a single young, which clings very tightly to the fur on its mother's stomach.

ENTELLUS LANGUR
Presbytis entellus

The Entellus Langur occurs from Pakistan and Nepal, throughout India to Sri Lanka. In India it has been considered sacred since ancient times, and sizeable groups of these langurs often live in towns on ornamental ledges or the walls of temples, raiding gardens and stealing fruit.

Entellus Langurs have a 70-cm-long body and a 100-cm-long tail. They live in large troops, often of over 120 animals, and on tree and bush-covered rocky mountain slopes they feed mainly on leaves, blossom and fruit with occasional insects. In the countryside langurs sleep in small caves.

The female gives birth to a single young, which clings tightly to its mother's stomach.

ASIATIC RED WOLF or DHOLE
Cuon alpinus

The Asiatic Red Wolf, or Dhole, is distributed from southern Siberia across China, central and southern Asia to Sumatra and Java. It is a powerful carnivore weighing approximately 20 kg and is 150 cm long, including its tail. Dholes live in packs in mountainous forests, up to a height above sea level of about 4 000 m. They hunt together by both day and night, their prey being deer, wild sheep and also fowl-like birds and reptiles, though they also catch molluscs and insects.

In her den, usually in a cave, the female has 2—9 pups.

Entellus Langur

Asiatic Red Wolf or Dhole

215

grows to a height of 80 cm and a weight of over 120 kg, with a 10-cm-long tail. It lives in mountain forests up to a height of 4 000 m, and in northern regions it is also found in taiga and tundra. It does not hibernate like other bears in winter. It forages for food in trees, and sometimes also sleeps in dense treetops. It eats birds' eggs and nestlings, wild bees' honey, various fruits, leaves and shoots. Only occasionally does it attack large animals, but it can kill a small horse or cow.

In June or July the male finds himself a mate, with whom he lives for several days. After a gestation period of 7—8 months, the female gives birth in a cave to 1—2 or occasionally up to 4 young. The cubs open their eyes after 3—4 weeks, and leave the den for the first time at the age of about 2 months.

LESSER PANDA
Ailurus fulgens

The Lesser Panda is about 110 cm long, including its 50-cm bushy tail. It is found in high mountains from Nepal to northern Burma and the south-west of China. Lesser Pandas live in forests and bamboo thickets. They feed mainly on bamboo shoots, but also eat sweet fruit, grass, roots, insects and the eggs or young of small birds. They have regular places in which to rest and sleep in

ASIATIC BLACK BEAR or MOON BEAR
Selenarctos thibetanus

The Asiatic Black Bear or Moon Bear is found over a huge area from eastern Iran, through India to China, Korea, Japan, Taiwan and central and eastern Siberia. It

Lesser Panda

216

Giant Panda

their territory, usually in a hollow tree or a cave or among dense branches.

In the den the female gives birth to 1—4 cubs, who are born blind, but open their eyes when they are 7—9 days old. The playful kittens leave the den after 45 days.

GIANT PANDA
Ailuropoda melanoleuca

The Giant Panda is found only in a small territory in the Hsifan Mountains of China's western Szechwan Province. These animals live in vast bamboo thickets, whose leaves and shoots form their main food. They sometimes also catch fish in brooks or hares among the rocks. Most of the year they lead a solitary life, pairing only for a short time during the mating season. The female has a single cub, which stays with her for 2—3 years. In winter, Giant Pandas hibernate in a den under the snow.

Adult Giant Pandas reach a length of 150 cm and a weight of 75—160 kg, and they are currently one of the rarest animals in the world.

SNOW LEOPARD or OUNCE
Uncia uncia

The Snow Leopard, or Ounce, is an inhabitant of the high mountains from eastern Turkestan to south-eastern Tibet, and northwards as far as the Aral Sea and Lake Baikal. It is a sturdy carnivore which weighs 23—41 kg and is about 2.5 m long, though its bushy tail is over 1 m in length. The Snow Leopard lives in the mountains at heights between 3 000 and 4 000 m, descending to lower land in winter. It is solitary, each leopard hunting in its own large territory. It makes its den in a cave, preferring to hunt at nightfall, when it lies in wait on a high vantage point from where it pounces on wild sheep, goats, wild hogs and deer. It also hunts hares, fowl and lizards.

217

In her den the female gives birth to 1—5 cubs.

WILD YAK
Bos mutus

The home of the Wild Yak is on the plateaux of Tibet, up to a height of 6 100 m. It is about 2 m tall and weighs about 500 kg.

The male Yak has horns up to 1 m long, the female's being shorter. Cows and calves live in small herds, and the bulls are solitary, though during the rutting season the males fight each other to obtain a herd of females. The young are born singly, and are able to stand up within half an hour of birth. Yaks live on grass, leaves, bamboo shoots, lichen and moss.

Wild Yak

218

The Yak was domesticated about 3 000 years ago, and has been raised by the natives of mountainous areas of Asia ever since. The cows yield only a small quantity of milk, but it is very nutritious and has a high fat content.

GORAL
Nemorhaedus goral

The Goral occurs from the Himalayas, through the whole of China to Korea and eastern Siberia. It grows to a height of up to 75 cm and a weight of about 30 kg. It is found mainly in rocky mountain districts, but also in low-lying scrub in semideserts. Gorals climb about the steep and stony slopes with great agility and speed, grazing on grass and browsing on the leaves of bushes.

In a sheltered place in the undergrowth the female gives birth to a single young, rarely to twins. After only an hour the young is able to stand, and the next day it is very active and follows its mother. It stays with her for 2 years.

MARKHOR
Capra falconeri

The home of the Markhor is in the mountainous regions of Uzbekistan and Tadzikistan in the USSR, Afghanistan, Kashmir and Pakistan. The male is 115 cm tall and weighs up to 120 kg, with very long spiral horns. The female is much smaller and lives in small herds with others and their young. The adult males mate with them in December, after which the females give birth to 1—2 young. Markhors live on grass, plants, leaves and twigs from bushes, and in winter on lichen and moss as well.

Goral

Markhor

Argali

Wild Goat

WILD GOAT
Capra aegagrus

The homeland of the Wild Goat stretches from the southern Caucasus to Pakistan, Iran and Turkey. The male is up to 105 cm tall and has huge horns, while the female is smaller with more slender horns. Wild Goats live in large herds on rocky slopes overgrown with juniper, bushes and deciduous trees. They live on grass, leaves and, in winter, moss and lichen. The mating season is from October to January, and males compete for herds of females in fierce combat. A female gives birth to 1 — 3 offspring.

The Wild Goat is one of the ancestors of today's domestic goat.

ARGALI
Ovis ammon

The Argali is the largest member of the sheep family. The male reaches a height of 125 cm at the shoulder and a weight of 230 kg, though the female is smaller with more delicate horns. Argali occur from the Altai mountains to western Mongolia. Herds of these wild sheep graze on the mountain slopes, eating grass, young plants and leaves of bushes. Females give birth to 1 or rarely 2 kids.

LAMMERGEIER or BEARDED VULTURE
Gypaetus barbatus

The Lammergeier, or Bearded Vulture, is one of the largest birds of prey, with a wingspan of about 280 cm and growing to over 125 cm in length. It is an inhabitant of central Asia and the Himalayas, but is also found in the south of Europe and northern Africa. Its main food is the carcasses of large wild and domestic mammals. As well as the meat, it also eats small bones and picks out the marrow from larger ones.

The birds build their nest on a rocky ledge from a pile of branches and scraps of hide, hair and bones, then the female lays 1—2 eggs. Both birds take turns at incubation and looking after the offspring.

BLACK VULTURE
Aegypius monachus

The Black Vulture is found in mountain regions from Asia Minor to central Asia and Tibet, and it occasionally also occurs in southern Europe. It is a huge bird of prey with a wingspan of about 2.8 m. It feeds mainly on the carcasses of large mammals, only occasionally hunting live prey — lizards, frogs or small mammals.

In mid-February, pairs of Black Vultures build their large nests, usually in juniper

Lammergeier or Bearded Vulture

Black Vulture

Himalayan Monal Pheasant

Satyr Tragopan
or Crimson Horned Pheasant

trees. The birds break off branches with their enormous beaks to make the nests. Both parents take turns to sit on the single egg, and both feed the young with regurgitated food.

HIMALAYAN MONAL PHEASANT
Lophophorus impejanus

The Himalayan Monal Pheasant lives in the extensive growths of rhododendron and sparse oak or birch forests of the mountains from eastern Afghanistan to Bhutan and southern Tibet. The splendidly-coloured male grows to a length of 70 cm and a weight of 2—2.4 kg, while the predominantly grey-brown female is smaller. Each cock bird has 2—3 hens. The nesting season is from April to June, when hens scrape out a shallow hollow beneath a bush, which they line with leaves, needles, grass and fea-

thers. Here they lay 4—6 spotted eggs. The mother incubates the eggs and looks after the chicks herself. The diet of the Himalayan Monal Pheasant consists of roots, berries, seeds, grass, insects, worms and other invertebrates.

SATYR TRAGOPAN or CRIMSON HORNED PHEASANT
Tragopan satyra

The Satyr Tragopan, or Crimson Horned Pheasant, lives on the wooded slopes of the mountains of the Himalayan and south Tibetan regions. It is about 65 cm long, and the fiery-feathered male spreads his colourful breast feathers and raises the blue horns above his eyes to impress the females.
His mate builds her nest on the ground, or in nests among the trees vacated by other birds. She lays 2—7 spotted eggs, which she incubates herself. Satyr Tragopans live on the young leaves of various plants, on berries, seeds, insects, spiders, worms and molluscs.

Lady Amherst's Pheasant

LADY AMHERST'S PHEASANT
Chrysolophus amherstiae

Lady Amherst's Pheasant lives in the mountain forests of western China and north-eastern Burma. The exquisitely coloured cock bird is up to 170 cm long, but 110 cm of this consists of his elongated tail feathers. One cock has 3—4 hens, which are greyish-brown with black wavy lines. Each hen lines a shallow depression beneath a bush with grass and leaves, and in it she lays 6—12 eggs. The mother incubates the eggs and protects and rears the chicks herself. This species feeds on seeds, green plants, berries, insects and their larvae, worms and molluscs.

ROCK DOVE
Columba livia

The Rock Dove occurs in rocky sites, particularly along valleys throughout south and south-east Asia. It is a wild ancestor of the domestic pigeon which is also frequently found in the large cities of Asia. Rock Doves, which are about 35 cm long, live in colonies of over 100 birds. Pairs of them build their nests in crevices in the rocks and caves, or in a hole in a palm tree, and in towns they sometimes nest on beams in attics, or in cracked walls. The nest is made of grass stalks and sticks, and here the female lays 2 white eggs, which both parents incubate. The parents at first feed the young with moist food regurgitated from their crops, later with pre-digested seeds. Adult birds forage in the morning and evening, mainly for seeds and green plants.

Rock Dove

REPTILES

TOKAY
Gekko gecko

The Tokay reaches a length of 40 cm and is one of the largest species of gecko. It lives in the whole of south-east Asia, and is found on rocks and among trees. In large cities such as Singapore it may be seen on the walls of buildings or in houses. Tokays spend the day hidden in their holes, and set out hunting in the evening. They climb deftly over smooth walls, and can walk upside down. This is made possible by their broad fingertips which have layers of scale-like suckers on the underside, allowing them to grip firmly. Tokays live on insects, spiders and centipedes, young mice, nestlings and smaller geckos.

In a sheltered crack in a rock, wall or tree the female lays 2 eggs, whose soft membrane rapidly hardens in the air. The young may take as long as 200 days to hatch, but they are immediately able to fend for themselves.

AMPHIBIANS

GIANT SALAMANDER
Megalobatrachus japonicus

The Giant Salamander is found in the mountain streams and small rivers of the Japanese islands of Hondo and Kyushu. It grows to a length of 150 cm, and is one of the largest amphibians in the world. It spends its whole life in water, hiding during the day beneath the overhang of the river-bank in a tangle of roots or among large stones. At night it patrols its territory, catching fish, frogs, crustaceans, molluscs, worms, insects and insect larvae. In the egg-laying season Giant Salamanders move upstream to faster-flowing, better oxygenated waters. In August or September the female lays two long, gelatinous strings of eggs, which are fertilized by the male in the water. The larvae hatch after 2 months, undergoing metamorphosis 3 years later, when they reach a length of about 20 cm.

Tokay

Giant Salamander

224

DESERTS
AND
PLAINS

Afghanistan, desert near Kandahar

MAMMALS

LONG-EARED HEDGEHOG
Hemiechinus megalotis

The Long-eared Hedgehog is a native of both sandy, bush-covered deserts and dry plains in central Asia and Afghanistan. It is about 30 cm long, with conspicuously long ears. During the day it hides, sleeping in a lair which it digs underneath the bushes. After dark it sets out to hunt for prey in its fixed territory. It catches locusts, beetles, grasshoppers, and small lizards and snakes. In a burrow lined with grass and leaves, the female gives birth to 1—5 young.

STEPPE PIKA
Ochotona pusilla

The Steppe Pika is found in rocky terrain in the plains and semideserts of Kazakhstan in the USSR. This hare-like mammal with a short tail is about 15 cm long, and is sometimes called the Piping Hare because of its shrill call. Steppe Pikas live in large colonies, digging burrows about 40 cm deep with two entrances and a nesting chamber. The nest is lined with leaves, hair and fine grass, and females give birth to 7—13 young, three or four times a year. Steppe Pikas live on grass and leaves, often digging out stores underneath stones, where they keep up to 8 kg of large leaves and plants.

BOBAK
Marmota bobac

The Bobak lives in the plains, semideserts and cultivated areas of central Asia. It is a large rodent, about 65 cm long, which lives in colonies. Each pair of Bobaks digs itself a deep burrow in the ground, with the entrances made on a slope or on elevated hillocks, to protect the nest from flooding by rainwater. Bobaks forage for food during the day, eating grass, leafy plants and roots, fruit and seeds, insects and birds' eggs. In the underground chamber the female gives birth to as many as 12 young at a time. The whole family hibernates together in the lair, which is lined with dry grass. Their body temperature falls to around 4—8° C, and the animals take only 2—3 breaths each minute, compared with the usual 16.

Steppe Pika

Long-eared Hedgehog

227

Bobak

Golden Hamster

GOLDEN HAMSTER
Mesocricetus auratus

The Golden Hamster is well known as a domestic pet, and is about 18 cm long, including the tail, which measures just over 1 cm. It was brought to Europe from Syria in 1930, when it was first domesticated. Its native home is in the Near East and from the Balkans to the eastern Caucasus, where its habitat is plains and semideserts. It spends the day sleeping in underground burrows which it digs for itself, going out after dark to look for food in the vicinity of its home.

Its diet consists of grass, green plants, seeds, and insects, worms and molluscs. In a lair up to 1 m below the ground, the female gives birth several times a year to 4—12 young.

COMMON MONGOOSE or NEWARA
Herpestes edwardsi

The Common Mongoose, or Newara, is famous for being an enthusiastic cobra-hunter. It is found over a wide area from the south and east of the Arabian peninsula

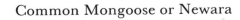

Common Mongoose or Newara

228

Przewalski's Horse

to India, Burma and Sri Lanka. Its thin body is about 50 cm long, its tail about 35 cm. It is found in plains and sandy, rocky, bush-covered areas, where it makes its home in holes in rocks or in the ground. Mongooses usually live in families or small groups, feeding mainly on small rodents, birds' eggs, insects and molluscs. They fearlessly attack even venomous snakes, moving quickly and seizing the snake behind the head so it cannot strike back. The struggle does not usually last long, for the mongoose soon kills its victim and eats it.

In her lair the female gives birth to 2—4 young.

PRZEWALSKI'S HORSE
Equus przewalskii

Przewalski's Horse is the only species of wild horse which can still be found in a natural habitat, though there are few of them remaining in the wild. It is a sturdy animal which reaches a height of up to 145 cm at the shoulders. An adult stallion, which is heavier than the mare, weighs up to 350 kg. Przewalski's Horse is distributed in southwest Mongolia, the Gobi Desert and on the plateaux of the Altai mountains, but there are few reliable reports of its being seen in recent times.

Przewalski's Horses live in small herds of 5—15 mares with their foals, led by a strong stallion. In times of danger this leader protects the mares and foals from enemies. For most of the year they graze on dry grass and plants or browse on the leaves and twigs of stunted bushes. After sunset they regularly set out for watering places and cannot survive for more than 3—4 days without water.

In spring the mare gives birth to a single foal weighing about 45 kg.

PERSIAN ONAGER
Equus hemionus onager

The Persian Onager, a subspecies of the Asiatic Wild Ass, is about 120 cm tall at the shoulders. It inhabits the plains and pla-

Persian Onager

Bactrian Camel

teaux of northern Iran and southern Turkmenistan in the USSR. Onagers live in small herds, led by a strong stallion. During the day they graze on grass, salt-tolerant plants and the leaves of small bushes, going to water-holes in the evening to drink.

Mares give birth to a single foal, which weighs 25—30 kg. For the first few days it hides in the undergrowth, but after a week it can run with the herd.

BACTRIAN CAMEL
Camelus bactrianus

The Bactrian Camel reaches a height of 230 cm at the shoulders and weighs up to 600 kg. Today it is best known as a domesticated animal, bred and kept widely in Asia and parts of south-eastern Europe. It still occurs in the wild in western Mongolia, the adjacent region of China and the east of central Asia. It can be found on upland plateaux at a height above sea level of 1 500 to 2 000 m. Its chief diet is grass, other green plants, fruit and twigs. In summertime, individual camels wander all over the plains, but in winter they form small groups of up to 20 and seek sheltered spots protected from the wind.

The female camel has a single young, which can stand up after only a few hours and in which two humps are already evident.

It is approximately 6 000 years since the Bactrian Camel was first domesticated in central Asia.

BLACKBUCK
Antilope cervicapra

The Blackbuck can be found in the plains and thin woodland of India. An adult male is 85 cm tall at the shoulders and weighs around 40 kg, although the female is smaller. Blackbucks normally live in groups of 15—20 animals, grazing on green vegetable food of all kinds.

The female usually has 1 offspring, rarely 2.

SAIGA
Saiga tatarica

The home of the Saiga is in Kazakhstan, Turkestan, southern Siberia, western Mongolia and north-west China. This antelope species grows to a height of 60—80 cm at the shoulders and weighs 36—63 kg. The males are larger and have horns, while the females have none. Saigas inhabit both treeless plains and semideserts, but also wander into cultivated fields. They live in huge herds, which wander over a large area in search of food, covering great distances and swimming across rivers in their path. They eat many different species of plants, even those which are poisonous to other animals. The onset of the breeding season is in November when there are protracted battles between males over females, the winner taking a herd of 5—50 females. At the end of spring a single offspring (or occasionally two) is born to the female under cover of long grass.

Blackbuck

Saiga

231

BIRDS

ASIAN KING VULTURE
Sarcogyps calvus

The Asian King Vulture lives in India and the western half of south-east Asia. It is a large bird of prey about 80 cm long, which lives in the open grassland of semideserts, on open mountain slopes or in thin woodland. These vultures live in pairs, feeding on the carcasses of large mammals, but they often fly to the outskirts of towns, where they seek domestic rubbish and decaying flesh on rubbish tips.

The pair usually builds its nest at the top of a spreading tree, or in semideserts even in a tall bush. The female lays a single egg, which both parents take turns to incubate and then they both feed the chick.

TAWNY EAGLE
Aquila rapax

The Tawny Eagle is widespread in the semideserts of central, eastern and southern Asia. This 75-cm-long bird of prey builds its large nest of branches and dry grass in an isolated tree or tall bush. The female lays 1—3 eggs, which she incubates herself, also having to find her own food, since the male does not feed her. Though both parents bring food for the young, the mother takes charge of dividing up the prey and feeding it to the offspring. The Tawny Eagle preys on rodents, young fowl-like birds, lizards and snakes.

Asian King Vulture

Tawny Eagle

DEMOISELLE CRANE
Anthropoides virgo

The Demoiselle Crane is the smallest and commonest crane species, growing to a length of 95 cm and a weight of 2.5 kg. Its home is in western and central Asia, but it is also found in Africa and southern Spain. The Asian birds migrate to India, Burma and the Red Sea coast in winter. The favourite habitats of Demoiselle Cranes are river valleys, grassy or stony plains and se-mideserts. They nest in grass on the ground. The female lays her 2 spotted eggs in a shallow scrape usually lined with grass stalks, and incubates them herself. The young, which run around as soon as they are dry, are looked after and led to seek food by both parents. The Demoiselle Crane lives on insects, especially locusts, and seeds, berries and green parts of plants.

BLUE-CHEEKED BEE-EATER
Merops superciliosus

The Blue-cheeked Bee-eater, which is about 30 cm long, is found from the Middle East to central, south and south-east Asia. During the nesting season the birds form nesting colonies and find clayey or sandy slopes or banks. In these, each pair digs a tunnel 1—2 m long, with a nesting chamber at the end. Here, on a thin lining of grass, the female lays 4—5 eggs, both parents take turns to incubate them and to feed the young. These birds catch their prey on the wing, eating wasps, bees and other insects.

ROSE COLOURED STARLING
Sturnus roseus

The Rose Coloured Starling is one of the best known and most useful birds of central Asia, which is found right up to the Persian

Demoiselle Crane

Blue-cheeked Bee-eater

233

Rose Coloured Starling

Gulf and Yugoslavia. The male and female, 21.5 cm long, have the same coloration. Large flocks of them are to be seen in plains and cultivated fields, but they also often fly into the desert in search of their main prey, the locust. They also eat other insects and mulberries.

Rose Coloured Starlings live in colonies of hundreds or thousands of birds even in the nesting season. They build their nests on cliff faces, in tree hollows, in haystacks or under the eaves of village houses. The nest is made of twigs, grass, straw and leaves, lined with roots and feathers. The female lays 5—7 eggs and incubates them herself, then both parents feed the young on insects.

REPTILES

FOUR-TOED TORTOISE
Testudo horsfieldii

The Four-toed Tortoise inhabits an area from the Caspian Sea to western Pakistan, and the shell of a mature adult is about 30 cm long. The animal is found in plains and semideserts up to a height above sea level of 1 200 m, where it lives on grass, plants, fallen fruit, and sometimes on animal prey such as insects. It winters in a burrow which it digs itself, or occasionally occupies a den deserted by other animals. In May or June the female lays 2—4 eggs, which she buries in the ground. The young are independent on hatching.

Four-toed Tortoise

Gecko *Teratoscincus scincus*

Indian Cobra

GECKO
Teratoscincus scincus

The Gecko *Teratoscincus scincus* lives in the deserts and mountain foothills of central Asia, preferring sandy regions sparsely covered with grass and low bushes. It digs a burrow about 80 cm long in loose earth, where it hides during the day. After nightfall this lizard crawls out of its lair and slowly searches its territory for insects and spiders.

In June the female lays 2 clutches of 2 eggs in the ground, and the young hatch after several weeks.

INDIAN COBRA
Naja naja

The Indian Cobra is found in a vast area from Iran, India and southern central Asia to south-east Asia, including Indonesia and the Philippines. Only in India does the cobra have the characteristic spectacle-like markings on its hood. The Indian Cobra grows to a length of up to 2 m, and is a highly dangerous snake with deadly venom. It always lives where it can find plenty to eat, so it is common in plains, semideserts and forest edges where there are large numbers of rats, mice and other rodents, which are its main food. It sinks its venom fangs into its victim, then swallows it whole. It is nocturnal, emerging only at night to seek its prey.

During the breeding season these snakes live in pairs. The female uses her snout to dig a passage in soft earth, with two entrances. In this lair she lays 10—20 eggs, which both parents take turns to guard. The young are independent from birth.

Indian snake-charmers use cobras in their shows, sitting in front of the erect snake and playing a pipe as the cobra seems to dance. In fact these snakes are deaf and unable to hear any music, and their movements are merely a reaction to the movements of the snake-charmer's pipe or hands.

Russell's Viper

RUSSELL'S VIPER
Vipera russelli

Russell's Viper occurs from India and Sri Lanka, through Burma and Thailand to Sumatra and Java. It may be up to 175 cm long, and is found in scrubland, gardens and parks. It is highly venomous, and its bite may be fatal. These vipers leave the shelter of holes to search for food only after dark, mainly hunting small rodents. The female gives birth to about 10 live young.

WATERS
AND
SWAMPS

Photograph by Oldřich Mazůrek

Central India, Deccan Plateau

238

MAMMALS

RUSSIAN DESMAN
Desmana moschata

The home of the Russian Desman is the river basins of the Volga, Don, Dneiper and Ob. It is an insectivore about 42 cm long, though about half of this is its flat, scaly tail. Desmans dig burrows with underwater entrances in river banks, where up to 8 adults live together in the dry underground lair. They are good swimmers, using both their legs and tails, and hunt mainly fish, but also amphibians, crustaceans, molluscs or insects, catching them after dark.
In her lair the female gives birth to 1—5 young, which are blind for the first 3 weeks.

MALAYAN TAPIR
Tapirus indicus

The Malayan Tapir is found in Sumatra, Malaysia and Thailand. It is a robust mammal, 130 cm tall at the shoulders, and weighing up to 300 kg. Its habitat is primary forests in river basins, and swampy places with lush vegetation. It pushes its way deftly and rapidly through thickets and reedbeds and can swim well; when in danger Malayan Tapirs will even dive below the surface. For most of the year they are solitary, only briefly forming pairs in the breeding season. The female gives birth to a single young in a dry, sheltered place in the undergrowth. These animals feed on leaves, grass, aquatic plants and fallen fruit.

INDIAN ONE-HORNED RHINOCEROS
Rhinoceros unicornis

The Indian One-horned Rhinoceros is an inhabitant of Assam, Nepal and Bengal in northern India. An adult may be 2 m tall at the shoulders and weigh 2 000—4 000 kg. These rhinoceroses are found in swampy jungles containing dense bamboo thickets and elephant grass, and like to be close to lakes or rivers, where they enjoy swimming and diving. They live in pairs or families, though old males are sometimes solitary. Their diet consists of grass, reeds, bamboo leaves and shoots, twigs and aquatic plants, especially water hyacinths.
The female has 1 or rarely 2 young.

Russian Desman

Malayan Tapir

Indian One-horned Rhinoceros

WATER BUFFALO
Bubalus arnee

The home of the Water Buffalo is from south and south-east Asia to Kalimantan (Borneo). This huge animal reaches a height of 180 cm at the shoulder and a weight of up to 820 kg. Its habitat is broad swamps and the banks of rivers and lakes, and it lives in herds, each defending its own terri-

Water Buffalo

tory. The female has a single calf, which stands up within half an hour. It is suckled for 6 months, but grazes from the age of 4 weeks. Adult buffalo eat leaves, grass, bamboo shoots and leaves, and swamp and aquatic plants. They feed mainly in the early morning and late afternoon, wallowing in mud or in shallow water during the heat of the day.

The Water Buffalo is kept as a domestic animal from Egypt, throughout tropical and subtropical Asia to the Philippines.

BIRDS

BLACK-NECKED STORK
Xenorhynchus asiaticus

The Black-necked Stork is distributed from India, through south-east Asia to New Guinea and Australia. It grows to a height of over 170 cm and a length of about 135 cm. It lives in swamps and on the banks of rivers and lakes, and in the nesting season pairs of storks defend a large territory. The parent birds share in building a nest at the top of a tall tree, then the female lays 3—5 eggs, sharing the incubation of them with her mate. Both parents also feed the young. Adult Black-necked Storks feed mostly on fish, but also on frogs, reptiles, crabs and other small animals.

BLACK KITE
Milvus migrans

The Black Kite is found throughout tropical and temperate Asia, but also in Europe and Africa. It is a bird of prey about 65 cm long, with a wingspan of 120 cm. Large flocks of these birds migrate southwards from the more northerly areas in autumn. Their preferred habitat is near large rivers, from the surface of which they like to collect dead fish, and they also hunt small mammals, reptiles, amphibians, insects and the occasional chicken.

During the breeding season they live in pairs, sharing in the building of a nest made of branches, sticks, leaves, roots and pieces of hide, in a tall tree. The female lays 2—4 spotted eggs, which she mostly incubates herself, then both parents feed the young.

Black-necked Stork

Black Kite

tail feathers up to 25 cm long. These birds make their home in marshes, swamps and lakes of lotus, and like to strut along large leaves floating on the water. They feed on insects, molluscs, seeds and water plants.

Pairs of jacanas make their nests of plant material among lotus leaves. The female lays 3—4 eggs, but they are incubated by the male, who also takes sole charge of the young while the female joins another male, producing as many as 10 clutches a year.

MALAYSIAN FISH OWL
Ketupa ketupu

The Malaysian Fish Owl, up to 50 cm long, is found in south-east Asia and the Greater Sunda Islands, living along the wooded banks of rivers and lakes, and in paddy fields. Fish Owls live in pairs, coming out after dark to sit on a dry branch, a high bank or a large stone sticking out of the water. From here they use their keen eyesight to spot fish or crabs in the shallows, seizing them in their powerful hooked claws. On land they catch lizards, snakes, small rodents and large insects.

Fish Owls make their nests in a hole in a large tree or a cave, usually above the wat-

PHEASANT-TAILED JACANA
Hydrophasianus chirurgus

The Pheasant-tailed Jacana inhabits south and south-east Asia. It is 30 cm long, but in the breeding season males grow elongated

Pheasant-tailed Jacana

er. The female lays 2—3 eggs, which she incubates herself while her mate keeps her supplied with food, and he also takes good care of the family after the young have hatched. Young Fish Owls begin to fly at the age of 10 weeks.

WHITE-BREASTED KINGFISHER
Halcyon smyrnensis

The White-breasted Kingfisher is distributed from the Middle East to south-east Asia and the Philippines, living close to rivers, streams and lakes. It feeds on land animals, grasshoppers, frogs and small lizards, and is also a skilful fisherman.
Each pair of birds digs itself a tunnel in a bank above or near to water. This ends in a nesting chamber, where the female lays 3—5 eggs, which she mostly incubates herself. Both parents feed the young, mainly on insects, and adult birds grow to 28 cm long.

REPTILES

CHINESE ALLIGATOR
Alligator sinensis

The Chinese Alligator is found on the lower reaches of the Yangtze River in eastern China. It reaches a length of 175 cm, and its feet are not webbed. It eats fish, molluscs and crustaceans, and the young feed on insects and spiders. These alligators spend the winter hibernating in holes scraped out of the bank, and their breeding habits remain largely unknown.

INDIAN GAVIAL
Gavialis gangeticus

The Indian Gavial is native to India, where it lives in the rivers Indus, Ganges, Mahana-

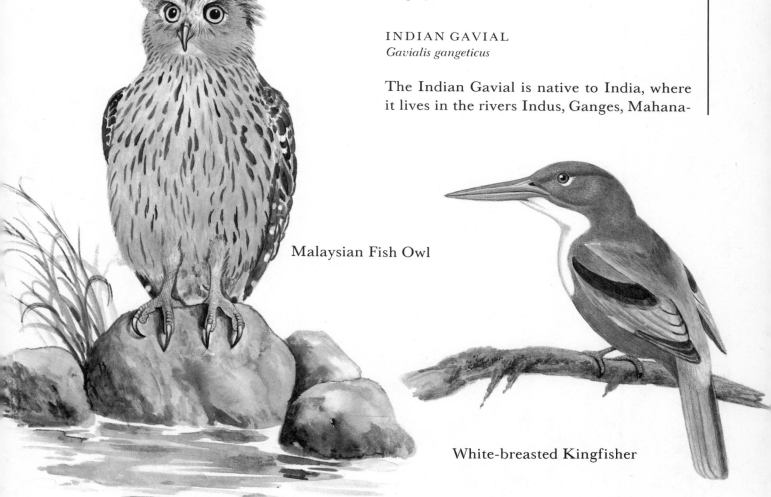

Malaysian Fish Owl

White-breasted Kingfisher

Chinese Alligator

Indian Gavial

di and Brahmaputra. Although it may grow to a length of 7 m and is one of the largest species of crocodile, it is not dangerous to man. Its main food is fish, and it only occasionally catches small mammals or birds. In its homeland it is a sacred animal, and no one may kill or disturb it.

The female lays about 40 eggs in a hole in a sandbank, larger and older females producing bigger clutches. The young hatch after 10 weeks.

RETICULATED PYTHON
Python reticulatus

The Reticulated Python, a native of southeast Asia, is one of the longest of the snakes, larger specimens growing to over 7 m long. It can devour mammals weighing 30 kg or more, and in Malaysia an 8-m-long python once seized and swallowed a pig weighing 72 kg. This is the largest prey known to have been taken by a snake. Usually, however, its prey are much smaller; it hunts rats, small wild pigs, young deer and other mammals, and birds.

In a sheltered place the female lays a clutch of 20 – 100 leathery eggs. She winds the coils of her body around them, which not only protects them, but also serves as an incubator. The young, which hatch after about 80 days, are able to fend for themselves at once, and the life span of these pythons averages 30 years.

Reticulated Python

EUROPE

Europe is the smallest of the continents except for Australia, though it is not an independent landmass, since it has a long border with Asia.

The European coastline is jagged, rocky in some places, with broad, sandy beaches in others. Many islands, both large and small, lie off the shores of Europe, the largest being Iceland, Great Britain and Ireland in the North Sea, and Sicily, Sardinia, Corsica and Crete in the Mediterranean to the south. There are many small islands close to the mainland in the Adriatic, Ionian and Aegean Sea regions. Small, uninhabited islands and inaccessible cliffs around the coast of northern Europe provide nesting-places for tens of thousands of sea birds every spring, and the seas in this area are a plentiful source of food for the birds and their young.

The warm Gulf Stream strongly influences the climate of western Europe, where winter is rainy, and not too cold, and summer is mild. Eastern Europe, on the other hand, has a continental climate, with very hot summers and harsh winters. Southern parts of the continent have a warm, subtropical climate, while the far north is a very cold, arctic region. The vegetation, too, varies according to the climate. The extreme north of Europe is covered by low tundra, and the topsoil thaws out only during the short summer season, when thousands of northern flower varieties come into bloom.

Lakes and pools, fed with water by the melting snows, attract large flocks of ducks, geese and other birds which come to nest. Southwards, the tundra gives way to thick coniferous and mixed forests, rich in game. Central Europe is characterized by mixed and deciduous forests, with spruce, fir, oak, beech, hornbeam and lime trees. Typical trees in the south are pine, fir, cypress, olive and fig.

Huge areas of Europe have been transformed by man, so the original landscape is today preserved in only a very few places. In the more densely populated areas it has been replaced by cultivated steppes and plains — agricultural fields, meadows and pastures. Instead of the original mixed forests, there are forests of spruce or pine only (monocultures), since these yield more timber. Elsewhere, people have brought about a complete change in the countryside by creating an artificial environment — towns and cities.

In the Forest

Since earliest times forests have provided human beings with both food and refuge. Wild animals were hunted for their meat and skins, and wood provided material for fires and primitive homes. The forests of Europe are still a refuge for many valuable species of game, but their main use is as a source of timber, without which life today would be difficult to imagine.

Present day forests in Europe are a mere fraction of the original vast expanses of woodland that covered the continent. Those forests have mainly been replaced by plantations of monocultures (usually conifers), since these grow faster than the primary forests and give a quicker turnover of timber. However, monocultures of conifers are less resilient than the original mixed growths. The trees are easily snapped or overturned by gales and snowstorms, and they are attacked by bark beetles, tortricid moths and other insect pests. They are also sensitive to smoke and other pollutants.

Forests affect the whole character of the countryside, and are above all an invaluable reservoir of water. This seeps slowly through the rich layer of loose topsoil, which is overgrown with moss, grass and other plants, down to the lower layers, to well up elsewhere in springs or to form lakes. The slow evaporation of water from the foliage of trees and undergrowth moistens the air, so that forests are very important for the climate of the whole region.

Photograph by Ivo Šlár

Water and Marshy Areas

Most streams and rivers rise in mountainous areas, where the greatest natural reservoirs of drinking water are to be found. Rivers are the home of many animals, the most important to humans being fish. Even some saltwater fish, such as the salmon and the eel, seek out cold, clear, fast-running freshwater streams in which to breed. Unfortunately, however, most European rivers are now inaccessible to such fish because of dams which have been built and industrial waste which pollutes the water. The lower, and often the middle, reaches of large European rivers are now regulated, their banks having been artificially reinforced.

The largest river in Europe is the Volga, which flows into the Caspian Sea. Next in size is the Danube, with its mouth on the Black Sea. A number of large rivers flow into the Atlantic Ocean, including the Rhine, the Seine and the Elbe, while the Rhone and the Po empty into the Mediterranean.

Areas with lakes and ponds have their own typical animal population. Every spring huge flocks of water birds fly to the large natural lakes which are to be found mainly in northern Europe, and many ducks, swans, grebes and gulls gather on artificial lakes and ponds.

Photograph by Oldřich Mazůrek

Fields and Meadows

In Europe nearly every suitable piece of land has been turned into crop-growing fields, making large areas of cultivated plains and steppes. Because of this, fields and pastures have become the homes of animals which originally lived in natural plains and steppes. Many animals, especially rodents such as voles, ground-squirrels and mice, which feed on cereals and other field crops, find conditions in cultivated plains ideal. In some years their numbers increase so much that they rob farmers of a large part of their harvest. Fortunately birds of prey such as kestrels, buzzards, owls and storks fly above the fields, keeping down the numbers of these pests. In addition, smaller birds catch large numbers of insect pests, such as the Colorado beetle.

Many meadows are also plant communities which have been formed mainly by humans. Only in the mountains or the far north do the meadows contain their original plants. In spring and summer meadows teem with thousands of flowers, which attract brightly-coloured butterflies, wasps, bees, spittle-bugs and flies, and in dry meadows there are also various species of grasshoppers. Meadows and fields near forests are visited in the evening, during the night and in the early morning by many woodland animals, such as deer and hares, which go there to graze.

Photograph by Ivo Šlár

In the Garden and Near People

Many animals have disappeared from the areas inhabited by human beings. Others have moved in closer to people. Some of these animals, especially those which breed in large numbers such as rats or mice, can be a nuisance. Some species of birds have also taken up residence close to human beings. The familiar sparrow, for example, often causes great damage to cereal crops. Some birds, such as the swallow, sometimes even make their homes inside buildings, in sheds, stables and outhouses. House martins and swifts often build their nests on the outsides of buildings, black redstarts in holes in walls. By hanging out nesting boxes people attract tits and also starlings. Blackbirds and thrushes, too, live near humans, nesting in gardens and on window-ledges. In towns and in cities you will find the nests of jackdaws and kestrels, while parks and orchards are made livelier by nuthatches, warblers, chaffinches and collared doves, even woodpeckers and, in western Europe, rock doves.

In winter, parks and gardens are visited by birds from the nearby countryside, which often come to feed from bird tables, driven by the harsh winter.

Photograph by Oldřich Mazůrek

Mountainous Regions

The mountains of Europe are an important source of water. At high altitudes there is heavy snowfall in winter, and when the spring thaw comes the melting snow feeds streams and rivers. Some of this water, however, is kept back by the mountain forests and peat-bogs, and this supplies the mountain springs throughout the summer. Another year-round source of water for the great rivers of Europe is the melting glaciers, such as those in the Alps.

The Alps are the highest mountain range on the continent, followed by the Pyrenees in the south-west and the Carpathians in eastern Europe. There are other high mountains in the very north, in Scandinavia, and in the Balkan peninsula.

The mountain areas of Europe have their own typical plants and animals, such as gentians, edelweiss, large growths of dwarf pine and stunted northern trees and shrubs. A characteristic Alpine animal is the ibex, and in many European mountains chamois and marmots can be found. Among the typical mountain birds of Europe are the Alpine chough, the nutcracker, the wall creeper, the rock partridge and the golden eagle. In the high mountains live insects which have adapted to life at great altitudes, where the summers are short.

Photograph by Ivo Petřík

EUROPE

MAMMALS

Badger
Bat, European Long-eared
Bear, Brown
Beaver, European
Boar, Wild

Cat, European Wild
Chamois

Deer, Roe
Dormouse, Edible

Fox, Red

Hamster, Common
Hare, Brown
Hedgehog

Ibex, Alpine

Lynx

Marmot, Alpine
Marten, Beech
Marten, Pine
Mole, European
Mouse, House

Noctule

Otter

Polecat

Rabbit, European
Rat, Black
Rat, Brown

Shrew, Water
Squirrel, European Ground
Squirrel, Red
Stoat

Vole, Common

Weasel
Wolf

BIRDS

Bittern, Eurasian
Blackbird
Bustard, Great
Buzzard, Common

Capercaillie
Chaffinch
Crane
Creeper, Wall
Crossbill, Red
Crow, Carrion
Cuckoo, Common

Dipper
Dove, Collared

Eagle, Golden

Goldcrest
Goose, Greylag
Goshawk
Grebe, Great Crested

Hoopoe

Jackdaw
Jay, Eurasian

Kestrel, Common
Kingfisher, Common

Magpie, Common
Mallard
Martin, House

Nightingale
Nightjar, Eurasian

Nutcracker
Nuthatch, Eurasian

Oriole, Golden
Ousel, Ring
Owl, Barn
Owl, Tawny

Partridge, Common
Partridge, Rock
Pigeon, Wood

Quail, Common

Raven
Redstart, Black
Robin, Eurasian
Rook

Shrike, Red-backed
Skylark
Sparrow, House
Starling, Common
Stork, White
Swallow
Swift, Common

Thrush, Song
Tit, Crested
Tit, Great

Woodpecker, Green
Wren, Common

REPTILES

Adder or Northern Viper

Slow-worm

AMPHIBIANS

Salamander, European Fire

253

Photograph by Ivo Šlár

Czechoslovakia, Jizerské hory Mountains

IN
THE
FOREST

───────

MAMMALS

NOCTULE
Nyctalus noctula

The Noctule is found throughout almost the whole of Europe, and is also common in Asia. It lives mainly in forests, though it can also be seen in large parks. During the day it rests in holes in trees or hangs on the rafters of barns, lofts and belfries. In summer about twenty of these bats can be found in one hole, while several hundred may sleep in a larger hole in the winter months. Noctules go hunting while it is still light, catching beetles and butterflies in mid-air. In summer, the female gives birth to 1 or occasionally 2 young, which cling to their mother's body for the first 10 days.

EUROPEAN RABBIT
Oryctolagus cuniculus

The original home of the wild rabbit is Spain. In the 13th century it was introduced to central Europe, where it bred rapidly and spread throughout almost the whole continent. Rabbits' favourite haunts are well-lit woodlands or wooded banks, and as they like warm places, they are not found at high altitudes. They dig burrows in the ground which they line with moss, grass and leaves. The female digs a special short burrow for the young, lining it with soft fur torn from her belly. She gives birth to 4—8 young up to five times a year. These are born blind and furless, opening their eyes only after 10 days. Rabbits look for food after sunset, feeding on grass, other vegetation, young bark and fallen fruit.

RED SQUIRREL
Sciurus vulgaris

The Red Squirrel lives mainly in woods and forests, but is also seen in city parks and gardens. It is found in most countries of Europe and the whole of Asia. It builds a round nest of twigs, leaves, moss and fur in a tree, often making its home in a hole in a tree or taking over the abandoned nest of a bird of prey. Here the female gives birth

Noctule

European Rabbit

Red Squirrel

to 3—6 young, which open their eyes after 4 weeks. Red Squirrels feed on nuts, berries, seeds taken from cones, and the shoots of conifers, but they also eat insects, birds' eggs and nestlings. In autumn they make themselves a winter store, but they do not hibernate, and can be seen even in snow.
The related Grey Squirrel has been introduced to Europe from America.

Edible Dormouse

EDIBLE DORMOUSE
Glis glis

The Edible Dormouse occurs throughout southern and central Europe, and eastwards as far as Asia Minor and Turkmenistan. Its main habitat is deciduous forests, but it is also seen in parks and gardens. During the day it sleeps in tree hollows or rock crevices, leaving its home after sunset to go in search of food. Dormice feed on seeds, the shoots of nut trees, and fruit, often raiding orchards. Insects and nestlings are also included in its diet. The female builds a nest of moss in the hollow of a tree, and gives birth to 2—9 young, which open their eyes after 20 days. Dormice become very much fatter in autumn, for they build up a supply of body fat to sustain them through their winter hibernation. They become active again in May.

EUROPEAN WILD CAT
Felis silvestris

The European Wild Cat lives in deep, dense forests, particularly in mountainous and hilly regions. It shelters in the hollows of large trees, in abandoned badgers' sets or in caves. Wild Cats live a solitary life for most of the year, pairing only during the mating season in February. The female gives birth in her den to 3—7 young, usually in April.

The newborn kittens are blind, opening their eyes only after 9—11 days. This Wild Cat preys mainly on mice, but it also hunts small birds, reptiles and insects, looking for its food at night.

LYNX
Felis lynx

The Lynx is found in central and northern Europe, in Asia and North America, living in large forests in both lowland and mountain areas. Lynxes are solitary, pairing only between January and March for the mating season. In April the female gives birth, in a shelter beneath an overhang or in a cave, to 2—5 spotted cubs. These are blind, opening their eyes after 16 days. The Lynx is a powerfully-built feline carnivore, weighing about 30 kg, though in Siberia and

European Wild Cat

257

Lynx

Wolf

Canada specimens may weigh up to 50 kg. Lynxes usually ambush their prey, leaping from the branch of a tree or from a vantage point on a rock. They hunt after dark, seeking small mammals and birds, and the males often prey on animals as large as roe deer.

WOLF
Canis lupus

Wolves are found in Europe, Asia and North America, living in forests or on bush-covered steppes. In spring and summer they form family groups, and in a den deep underground the female gives birth to 4—8 cubs about 2 months after mating. The young are born blind, opening their eyes after 10 days. During the first few days the she-wolf does not leave her cubs for a moment, and they are brought food by the male. Wolves hunt mammals and birds, but also eat molluscs, insects and even forest fruit. In winter, when they hunt in large packs, they attack large wild and domestic animals, but they avoid encounters with humans.

RED FOX
Vulpes vulpes

The Red Fox is the most common canine carnivore in Europe, and also occurs in Asia and North America. Foxes are mainly woodland creatures, but sometimes make their homes in large, thickly overgrown urban parks. They often scout round villages and isolated houses where poultry is kept, stealing hens and ducks in the night. Their main diet, however, is small rodents and birds; they also eat insects and molluscs, and in summer they gather woodland fruit. Foxes dig burrows, called earths, with a number of entrances, in a sheltered spot. There the fe-

Red Fox

Badger

Pine Marten

male gives birth to 4—12 cubs, which open their eyes after 12—15 days.

PINE MARTEN
Martes martes

The Pine Marten lives in forests throughout Europe and in a large part of Asia. Including its tail, it is about 80 cm long. During the day it stays in holes in trees, going hunting after sunset or in the early morning. Martens like to stalk squirrels or other small mammals and birds. They sometimes also catch insects, and in autumn they like to eat fruit and sweet berries. Usually in April, the female gives birth to 2—7 young in the hollow of an old tree, and the newborn Pine Martens open their eyes about 1 month later.

BADGER
Meles meles

The Badger lives mainly in woodland and on bush-covered slopes, but it can occasionally be found in large, overgrown urban parks. It is a heavily-built carnivore, weighing about 20 kg, which lives in family groups. They dig themselves deep dens called sets, with several long passages and ventilation shafts leading to the surface. The living-quarters are lined with moss and leaves. Badgers hunt after dark, catching small mammals, frogs and molluscs, and eating birds' eggs, or making do with worms, fallen acorns, roots and raspberries or strawberries. They like to dig up the nests of bees or wasps and eat their honey. Females give birth to 2—6 blind cubs, which open their eyes after 3—4 weeks. Badgers are less active during the winter, and in northern areas they may hibernate during the coldest weather, occasionally waking up and leaving their sets to eat.

BROWN BEAR
Ursus arctos

The Brown Bear is the largest European carnivore and may weigh up to 350 kg. It is found in deep mountain and highland forests, making its den in large hollows beneath fallen trees, or in caves. Here the female gives birth, usually in January, to 2—3 cubs, or occasionally up to 5. The cubs are born blind, opening their eyes after 4—5 weeks. The mother bear takes good care of them, not leaving the den for several weeks, during which time she lives off her body fat.

Brown Bear

When the cubs are four months old, their mother takes them out for the first time. Brown Bears are omnivorous, eating woodland fruit, roots, invertebrates, birds and birds' eggs, reptiles, mammals and often also carrion. They are good fishermen too, but their favourite food is bees' honey.

WILD BOAR
Sus scrofa

The Wild Boar is widespread in large forest areas with dense undergrowth. It lives in family herds, while older males are solitary. Wild Boars hide in thickets during the day and go out to feed at dusk. They gather forest fruit, nibble grass and pull up roots, making expeditions into potato and beet fields in autumn. They also pull up worms, eat molluscs and insects, plunder the nests of ground-nesting birds for their eggs or young, and are keen hunters of reptiles, especially snakes.

The sow has 3—12 horizontally-striped offspring, which she leads about and protects from predators. The Wild Boar, which weighs up to 200 kg, is the ancestor of the domestic pig.

ROE DEER
Capreolus capreolus

The Roe Deer is distributed throughout Europe and the temperate zone of Asia, inhabiting forests, bush-grown meadows and thickets around water. Roe Deer do not form herds, but are found singly or in small groups. In May or June the female has 1, 2 or occasionally 3 young, which hide in tall grass. The mother comes to suckle them every evening, staying nearby during the day to watch over them.

Roe Deer reach a weight of 15—35 kg. At the end of January the males grow small antlers, which are usually shed in November. These deer feed on grass, other vegetation, fruit and bark.

Wild Boar

BIRDS

RAVEN
Corvus corax

The Raven is a large member of the crow family, with a wingspan of 120 cm. It is resident in Europe, Asia and North Africa, living in forests or rocky places, often high in the mountains, though in the north it is found in lowland tundra and in eastern Europe and Asia it often nests on buildings. Ravens live permanently in pairs, and often as early as February, the female builds a large nest of twigs, moss and grass in a tree, on a cliff or on a high tower. She lays 4—6 eggs, which she mainly incubates herself, then both parents feed the young. Ravens are omnivorous, but prefer a meat diet. They feed mainly on the carcasses of large animals, and also hunt small vertebrates and invertebrates.

CARRION CROW
Corvus corone

The Carrion Crow, which is about 47 cm long and has a wingspan of about 1 m, is common throughout Europe. In western

Roe Deer

Europe the species is black all over, while in eastern Europe a subspecies known as the Hooded Crow, with a grey back and under parts, is found. During the nesting season crows usually frequent woodlands, large parks or avenues of trees, where they build their nests in high trees during March. The basic material used is twigs and tufts of grass, lined with moss and hairs. The female incubates the 4—6 eggs alone, while the male brings her food, then both parents feed the young. Crows feed mainly on scraps of meat, various small animals, seeds and berries. In autumn families congregate to make up large flocks, which roam the countryside.

EURASIAN JAY
Garrulus glandarius

The Eurasian Jay is found in the whole of Europe except for northern Scandinavia,

Raven

Carrion Crow

261

Eurasian Jay

Golden Oriole

Eurasian Nuthatch

and it also occurs in north-west Africa, Asia and eastwards as far as China. It is 34 cm long and has a wingspan of 54 cm. Its usual habitat is woodlands with a predominance of oak trees. It builds its nest of dry twigs, stalks, roots and moss in May or June, usually at the edge of the woods in the thick branches of a spruce. The female lays 5—7 eggs, which she takes turns with her mate to incubate. 3 weeks after hatching the young jays leave their nests and roam the woods with their parents. They have a mixed diet of vegetable and animal foods.

GOLDEN ORIOLE
Oriolus oriolus

In late spring the melodious, flute-like tones of the male Golden Oriole can be heard from the treetops in deciduous woods. This splendid bird occurs in all of Europe except for the British Isles and Scandinavia. In June Orioles weave a cradle-shaped nest of long stalks and strips of bark in the fork of a branch. The 3—5 eggs are usually incubated by the female alone, while the young are fed by both parents. Orioles feed on insects, spiders and soft berries, and also like to fly to orchards in search of ripe cherries. They migrate southwards as early as August, wintering in East or West Africa.

EURASIAN NUTHATCH
Sitta europaea

The Eurasian Nuthatch is a lively bird about 14 cm long, which is distributed throughout Europe, Asia and north-west Africa. It is found in woods, parks and large gardens. Nuthatches are winter residents, and during the cold months will even visit bird-tables. At the end of April the female lays 6—8 eggs on a nest lining of bark or

Red Crossbill

Crested Tit

dry leaves in a hole in a tree or a nesting-box. If the entrance is too wide, the Nut-hatch will make it smaller with little balls of earth mixed with saliva, which set rock-hard, helping to keep enemies out of the nest. The female incubates the eggs herself, but both parents feed the young. The Nut-hatch's diet consists of insects and insect larvae, spiders and other invertebrates, and in winter also various seeds.

RED CROSSBILL
Loxia curvirostra

The Red Crossbill, which grows to 16.5 cm long, inhabits coniferous forests in Europe, northern Asia and North America. The male is red, while the female is greenish in colour. This bird is conspicuous for its curved, crossed beak, ideal for extracting the seeds

from the cones of various conifers. The thick-walled nest is built in a tree by the female, using stalks, moss and lichen. Usu-ally in January or February she lays 3—4 eggs, which she incubates herself. During this time and in the first few days after the eggs hatch, while the mother warms her young, the male feeds them. Because the nesting season is so cold and frosty, the fe-male cannot leave either the eggs or the newly-hatched young even for a moment. When the young grow older and leave the nest, they join their parents and fly about the countryside in large flocks.

CRESTED TIT
Parus cristatus

The 11.5-cm-long, beautiful Crested Tit is found mostly in the coniferous forests of

263

Goldcrest

Common Wren

Europe. It nests in tree hollows, hollow tree-stumps or abandoned squirrels' nests. In a lining of moss and animal hairs, the female lays 5—11 eggs in April, incubating them herself. The young, which leave the nest at the age of 20 days, are fed by both their parents. Crested Tits eat insects and insect larvae, and also small seeds in winter.

GOLDCREST
Regulus regulus

The smallest of the European birds, the Goldcrest, inhabits the coniferous forests of almost the whole of the continent. It weighs 5—6 g and is only 9 cm long. Goldcrests sometimes gather in flocks in parks during the winter, and their gentle twittering can be heard from the treetops. Pairs of birds build their round nests at the end of April in the dense branches of conifers, using small twigs, stalks, spiders' webs and moss. The female incubates the 8—11 eggs herself, then both parents feed the young on aphids, small caterpillars and spiders. The young fly

2 weeks later. In winter Goldcrests pick insect eggs and pupae from the branches.

COMMON WREN
Troglodytes troglodytes

The tiny Common Wren, weighing only about 8—9 g, is found in woodlands throughout Europe. In winter it lives a solitary life, often visiting villages, where it seeks out insects and spiders in the crevices of stone walls or in piles of wood. In spring the male builds several nests with narrow side-entrances, from stalks, small twigs and moss. His mate then chooses the most suitable of these, lines it with hairs and feathers, and lays 5—7 eggs there.

EURASIAN ROBIN
Erithacus rubecula

The Eurasian Robin, which is 14 cm long, is found in woods and large parks throughout almost the whole of Europe, eastern Siberia and North Africa. It is partially migrant,

Eurasian Robin

Green Woodpecker

leaving more northerly regions in October for North Africa or south-west Europe, though many old male birds do not leave their homes in winter. During this period they feed mainly on berries. In April the female builds a nest among stones, beneath roots, in discarded cans or containers, or even on a shelf in an outbuilding, using roots and stalks and lining it with animal hair. She incubates the 5 eggs herself, and both parents feed the young on insects, insect larvae and spiders.

GREEN WOODPECKER
Picus viridis

The 32-cm-long Green Woodpecker is common throughout most of Europe, living in deciduous woodlands, parks, orchards and other wooded areas. Its ringing voice is heard from early spring. At the end of April these woodpeckers chisel a hole about 50 cm deep in the trunk of a tree, where the female lays 5—7 eggs, taking turns with her mate to incubate them. When the young

hatch, the parents feed them mostly on ants and ant pupae. Green Woodpeckers also eat the larvae of beetles which cause damage beneath the bark of trees.

EURASIAN NIGHTJAR
Caprimulgus europaeus

The Eurasian Nightjar arrives in Europe in May from its far-off wintering places in East and southern Africa. It is a nocturnal bird, about 27 cm long, and is distributed throughout almost the whole of Europe, Asia and Morocco. Its habitat is sparse, dry coniferous or mixed forests with a predominance of pines. Throughout the day it perches motionless in a tree, its shape and colour resembling the stump of a branch.

Eurasian Nightjar

Tawny Owl

Usually in June, the female lays 2 eggs on the bare ground, and both parents incubate them. They feed the young at night, for about a month, with beetles and moths which they catch in the air. In August or September they set off again for the south.

TAWNY OWL
Strix aluco

The Tawny Owl is one of the most common of European owls. It is 38 cm long, with a wingspan of 94 cm, and is resident, even in the coldest winters. It lives in woods, parks and large gardens, usually nesting in holes in trees, but also among the rafters of barns, belfries and derelict buildings. In April the female lays 3—5 eggs, which she incubates herself. During the first 10 days after they have hatched, the male feeds the whole family on small vertebrates such as voles, frogs or bats, and they also eat insects. Tawny Owls hunt by night.

COMMON CUCKOO
Cuculus canorus

The voice of the male Cuckoo can be heard from the end of April, when the bird returns from far-off tropical or southern Africa. The females follow some days later. Cuckoos are found in almost the whole of Europe, Asia and Africa. They inhabit woods, parks, bushy places and large patches of reeds by the waterside. Females fly around their territory in search of the nests of small songbirds. When they find a suitable one, they throw out one of the eggs and replace it with one of their own. 12 days later the young Cuckoo hatches, and removes all the remaining eggs or young of its unwilling foster-parents, which feed it on insects and

Common Cuckoo

Common Buzzard

Goshawk

insect larvae. The young Cuckoo is insatiable, with its beak constantly open wide, waiting for food. Adult birds feed on caterpillars, beetles, butterflies and spiders. At the end of August Cuckoos fly far to the south again.

COMMON BUZZARD
Buteo buteo

The Common Buzzard, a bird of prey with a wingspan of about 130 cm, is found throughout Europe and in Asia and the Far East. It lives in forests of all kinds, preferring to nest near meadows and fields. Here it hunts voles and mice, and so performs a useful function. It is mostly resident, but birds from more northerly regions fly to the south-west in winter. In April each pair of Buzzards builds a nest of branches, leaves and moss in a tall tree, or sometimes on a cliff. The female incubates the 2—4 eggs herself, and also feeds the young for the first few days with prey which the male passes to her.

GOSHAWK
Accipiter gentilis

The Goshawk, a bird of prey 55 cm long and with a wingspan of up to 140 cm, is

267

Wood Pigeon

Capercaillie

found in Europe, Asia, North America and Africa. It lives exclusively in forests, where each pair has a territory about 5 km across. The birds usually build their large nest in April, in the crown of a pine or spruce, using sticks and twigs. In it the female lays 3—4 eggs, which she mostly incubates herself. For the first 10 days the mother does not leave her young for a moment, and the male feeds the whole family. He passes the prey to his mate, who tears it apart and gives the young pieces of meat. The Goshawk mainly hunts birds up to the size of herons, and also catches small mammals.

WOOD PIGEON
Columba palumbus

The Wood Pigeon, weighing about 500 g and about 40.5 cm long, is an inhabitant of most of Europe, the temperate zone of Asia, and north-west Africa. In warmer regions it

is resident, but it migrates from more northerly areas to winter on the Mediterranean. It mainly inhabits woodland, but in western Europe it is also found in parks and gardens. Wood Pigeons usually build their nests of a few dry twigs on the branch of a conifer, then the female lays 2 eggs, sharing their incubation with her mate. At first the parents feed the young on 'pigeon's milk', a special paste which they make in their crops. Wood Pigeons feed mainly on seeds and green plants, and sometimes on insects, worms and molluscs.

CAPERCAILLIE
Tetrao urogallus

The great forests of northern and central Europe and Asia are the home of the Capercaillie. The male weighs up to 6 kg, the dull-coloured female only 3 kg. Capercaillies remain in their territories all the year round. In spring the males compete for females, and their typical mating calls can be heard.

Cock birds take no part in the business of nesting, but the hen makes a shallow depression near the trunk of a tree and lines it with grass and leaves. She incubates the 5—8 eggs herself, and also takes sole care of the chicks, leading them about with her in search of food, and protecting them. Capercaillies feed on insects, berries, buds, the topmost twigs of conifers and on a variety of green plants and seeds.

REPTILES

SLOW-WORM
Anguis fragilis

Slow-worms are often found in woods, parks and gardens. This limbless, innocuous lizard grows to a length of about 50 cm. During the day it hides under stones or in holes, or suns itself close to its shelter. At twilight it sets off in search of food, catching insects, worms, slugs and centipedes. At the end of July the female gives birth to 5—26 live young. In October Slow-worms find themselves a place in which to hibernate, under a large stone, in a hole in the ground or in a crevice in the rocks, several dozen of them often spending the winter together. At the end of March or in April, when the weather is fine, they wake up and leave their winter home.

ADDER or NORTHERN VIPER
Vipera berus

The Adder, or Northern Viper, occurs in woods, steppes, grassy fields and bushy places from the British Isles to Japan. It grows to a length of 80 cm, and is highly venomous. The bite is especially dangerous to young children, but Adders never attack of their own accord, preferring to hide from man. They usually go hunting in the evening, when they eat voles and mice, thus being very useful. At the end of August the female gives birth to 6—20 live young. In October Adders seek places in which to hibernate, in holes or crevices among rocks, coming out again in the second half of April.

Adder or Northern Viper

Slow-worm

AMPHIBIANS

EUROPEAN FIRE SALAMANDER
Salamandra salamandra

The strikingly-coloured European Fire Salamander lives in deciduous forests with clear-flowing streams. This black and yellow amphibian spends the day in damp moss or under stones. After rain it leaves its shelter even during the day, but it normally goes in search of food only when evening falls, hunting earthworms, slugs, insects and spiders. In April or May the female seeks out springs or pools beside streams, where she deposits up to 70 larvae about 3 cm long, which have four legs and gills. 2—4 months later the larvae complete their metamorphosis, the gills having disappeared, and the young salamanders leave the water. European Fire Salamanders spend the winter in deep holes or in cracks in the ground.

European Fire Salamander

WATER
AND
MARSHY
AREAS

Photograph by Oldřich Mazůrek

Czechoslovakia, northern Bohemia

MAMMALS

WATER SHREW
Neomys fodiens

The Water Shrew lives in the whole of Europe and in northern and central Asia. It grows to a length of 7—11 cm, and is found near both still and running water, where it digs a burrow in the bank. It is an agile insectivore, darting about at the water's edge all night and catching insects. Water Shrews also catch small fish, newts, crustaceans, worms and molluscs in the water. In a den softly lined with grass and moss the female gives birth to 4—10 blind young, which open their eyes after 3 weeks. Water Shrews are active throughout the winter.

OTTER
Lutra lutra

The Otter is found in rivers, streams and still waters in Europe, Asia and North America. It is a carnivore about 130 cm long, adapted to an aquatic life and feeding on crayfish, molluscs, frogs, fish, small mammals and birds. Otters dig their burrows into the bank, with an underwater entrance and one or two ventilation shafts. In a dry chamber in the burrow, lined with grass and leaves, the female gives birth to 2—6 young, which open their eyes after 4 weeks. If kept in captivity from an early age, Otters can be as tame as dogs.

EUROPEAN BEAVER
Castor fiber

The European Beaver was once found in the whole of Europe, but it now occurs in sizable numbers only in the north and north-east. It is a rodent of 1 m in length, including its tail, and it lives on the banks of still or sluggish waters, where it builds dams

Water Shrew

Otter

European Beaver

of branches. Beavers live in pairs, but these join up to form larger groups. At the end of April the female gives birth in her burrow, or lodge, to 2—7 young, which are sighted from birth. Beavers go out at night to feed on various plants and twigs. They also fell trees in order to nibble the soft bark of their branches. They build up a winter store of branches under the water, taking them mainly from poplars and willows.

BIRDS

DIPPER
Cinclus cinclus

The Dipper is found not only in Europe, but also in Asia and north-west Africa. It is an 18-cm-long songbird, occurring mainly in mountainous regions, near streams and small rivers where it hunts for its food. Entering the water, it runs about on the river-bed, using its wings like oars. It catches insect larvae and small crustaceans beneath the water, using its beak to roll away the small stones beneath which large numbers of freshwater shrimps lie hidden. Dippers build their nests in hollows near the water from pieces of aquatic plants and wet moss. The female lays 4—6 eggs, which she incubates herself, then both parents feed the young.

NIGHTINGALE
Luscinia megarhynchos

The Nightingale is one of the best known European birds because of its song. This is particularly striking at night, but Nightingales sing even in the daytime. Their habitat is close to water and in deciduous lowland forests near rivers. Their nests, built of stalks, roots, moss and hair, are constructed in thickets close to the ground. The female lays 5—6 eggs, which she incubates for 13 days. When the young are 11 days old, they jump out of the nest, but it is several more days before they start to fly. Nightingales feed on insects, worms and spiders. They

Dipper

Nightingale

274

migrate to North and tropical Africa in August, returning to Europe in April.

COMMON KINGFISHER
Alcedo atthis

The Common Kingfisher makes its home in Europe and in Asia, where it is among the commonest birds especially in the tropics. It is about 16.5 cm long, with conspicuous colouring. It is resident even in winter, when it travels over a large area. At the nesting season it looks for either still or running water with steep banks. In one of these it digs a burrow about 1 m long with its beak, lining the nesting chamber with fish scales. Usually in May, the female lays 5—8 eggs, and her mate sometimes takes turns to incubate them. Both parents feed the young on insects, small crustaceans and fish, and while hunting, Kingfishers often dive into the water.

Common Kingfisher

GREAT CRESTED GREBE
Podiceps cristatus

The Great Crested Grebe, about 48 cm long, is distributed in Europe and in Africa, Asia and Australia, living on lakes and large fish-

CRANE
Grus grus

The Crane is found in marshy regions of northern Europe and northern Asia. This long-legged bird, which has a wingspan of 220 cm, also nests occasionally in the north of central Europe and in Spain. European birds spend the winter in Africa, on the banks of the Nile. In spring, during their courting rituals, the birds hoot loudly and jump about as if they are dancing. They make their nests of reeds and sticks on an island or on flattened reeds in marshland. Usually in May, the female lays 2 eggs, taking turns with her mate to sit on them. As soon as they have hatched out and dried off, the young run about and can swim. Cranes feed on seeds, green plants, insects, molluscs, and occasionally small vertebrates.

Crane

Great Crested Grebe

MALLARD
Anas platyrhynchos

The mallard is found wherever there is water, almost all over the world. It even makes its home on small ponds in city parks. They live in pairs, and their nests are built by the female in sheltered places in the grass by the waterside, but the male chooses the site. The mother bird incubates the 8—14 eggs by herself, and also takes sole charge of the ducklings. Mallards feed on grass, seeds, insects, small crustaceans, worms and molluscs. In winter large flocks of them are often found in cities, where they can find plenty of food.

GREYLAG GOOSE
Anser anser

The home of the Greylag Goose is in Scotland, Iceland, the coast of Scandinavia, and some parts of central Europe, but it also lives in the north of Asia. In March these geese return from south-western Europe and North Africa to their breeding grounds, where each pair has its own territory. The female builds a nest of plant material, usually among reeds or on an island. She sits on the 4—9 eggs herself for 27—30 days, with

ponds where there are extensive areas of reeds. It flies to its European nesting-places in March or April, and builds a tall nest of water plants among dense reeds. Both parents incubate the 3—6 eggs, then the parent birds often carry small chicks among the feathers on their backs, feeding them on insects and molluscs. Adult birds feed mainly on small fish and insect larvae.

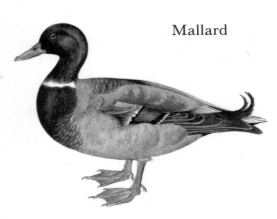

Mallard

Greylag Goose

the male keeping watch nearby. Both geese then look after the goslings, taking them in search of food. Greylag Geese attain a length of about 82 cm, and feed on green plants and on seeds. They are ancestors of the domestic goose.

EURASIAN BITTERN
Botaurus stellaris

The Eurasian Bittern is a member of the heron family. It is about 75 cm long, and lives in Europe, northern Asia and North Africa. On warm spring evenings its booming voice can be heard announcing its territory in marshes and large reed beds. In May, these birds build large nests of stalks on flattened reeds, where the female lays and incubates 4—6 eggs. The mother also looks after the young herself, in the early days regurgitating food for them into the nest. Bitterns feed on insects, frogs, fish and some plant material. In September they fly from colder regions to western Europe or North Africa.

Eurasian Bittern

Czechoslovakia, foothills of the Giant Mountains

FIELDS
AND
MEADOWS

BROWN HARE
Lepus capensis europaeus

The home of the Brown Hare is in fields, on bushy banks and in sparse woodland. An adult hare weighs 4—8 kg. Between February and September females give birth up to five times, to 2—7 young, which can see at birth and run about at once. Hares do not dig burrows, but rest in the open, in shallow depressions called 'forms', each hare making its own in the grass. Hares set out in search of food after dark, eating grass, a variety of other green plants, grain and in winter bark. They can run very fast to escape from their many enemies, reaching a speed of about 65 km per hour. They are also quite good swimmers, and can swim for some time.

COMMON HAMSTER
Cricetus cricetus

The Common Hamster is distributed from France through central Europe, as far as the river Yenisei in the USSR. It is a rodent about 35 cm long, living in fields, dry meadows and steppes in an underground burrow. It digs several entrances and exits to the burrow, and goes in search of food after dark, bringing it home in its cheek pouches. Its main food is plant material, and it causes considerable damage to crops, but also eats invertebrates and small vertebrates. In a lined chamber of the underground lair the female gives birth to 4—18 young. Hamsters build up a large store of grain in their burrows to see them through the winter. They hibernate from October to March, but wake up at intervals, eat their fill and then go back to sleep again.

Brown Hare

Common Vole

Common Hamster

European Ground Squirrel

EUROPEAN GROUND SQUIRREL
Citellus citellus

The European Ground Squirrel lives on steppes, in fields and on grassy banks from the eastern half of central Europe to China. It attains a length of about 28 cm, 6 cm of which is tail. It digs a burrow in the ground, 1—4 m deep and 7 m long. Here the female gives birth to 6—11 blind young, which open their eyes from the age of 4 weeks. The European Ground Squirrel's diet is made up of seeds, plants, insects and molluscs. It hibernates from October to April, but without any winter store, living off its body fat.

COMMON VOLE
Microtus arvalis

The Common Vole, a small rodent, occurs throughout continental Europe except in Scandinavia and the extreme south. It is absent from the British Isles, except Orkney and Guernsey. In some years, usually about every fourth, voles breed in incredible numbers. At such times each female may give birth to 3—13 young as many as twelve times a year. Voles in such large numbers cause great damage to growing crops. Voles dig tunnels in the ground, with chambers about half a metre below the surface, and narrow passages lead up to the open air. It is along these that the voles crawl to go in search of grass, root and cultivated crops. These voles do not sleep through the winter, but make tunnels beneath the snow.

BIRDS

ROOK
Corvus frugilegus

The Rook, which is about 46 cm long, is found in almost the whole of Europe and in areas of Asia north of the Himalayas. In winter huge flocks of Rooks fly about the countryside, often going into the parks and gardens of large towns. In early spring they return to their breeding grounds in forests, or in parks, living in large colonies even at this time of year. Individual pairs build their nests in trees. The female lays 4—5 eggs, which she incubates herself, both parents then feeding the young. Rooks feed mainly on insects, meat scraps and seeds.

Rook

281

Common Magpie

COMMON MAGPIE
Pica pica

The Common Magpie, about 46 cm long, is found throughout Europe, Asia, North America and North Africa. It is a resident bird, whose favourite haunts in Europe are bushy slopes and the shrub-covered banks of ponds. At the beginning of April pairs of these birds work together to build a nest in a tall bush, using branches and lining it with tufts of grass and earth. They also make a roof of thorny twigs over the nest. The female usually incubates the 3—10 eggs for 18 days, then the young are fed by both parents. Magpies eat invertebrates, small rodents, birds, seeds and berries. They are well known for their love of bright objects, which they pick up and hide in various secret places.

SKYLARK
Alauda arvensis

The 18-cm-long Skylark is found both in lowlands and high in mountains. It flutters high in the air in one spot, its lilting song carrying over a wide area. This is how the male informs other birds that the territory is his. Skylarks build their nests of roots and pieces of leaves on the ground. The female

Skylark

Common Kestrel

Great Bustard

lays 3—6 eggs, incubating them for 2 weeks, then both parents feed the young on insects, spiders and small slugs. Adult birds also eat seeds. European Skylarks migrate to the south of the continent in October and November, returning in February.

COMMON KESTREL
Falco tinnunculus

The Common Kestrel occurs in Europe, Asia and Africa, and is about 34 cm long. It is a highly useful small bird of prey, hunting harmful rodents, sparrows and insects. Kestrels can often be seen hovering over meadows and fields looking for prey. During the last decade they have been moving more and more into large towns, where they nest in church towers and on ledges outside buildings.
The female lays 5—7 eggs. During the early

days after they hatch, the male brings food for the young, but the mother bird divides it up and feeds it to them. Later the female also hunts.

GREAT BUSTARD
Otis tarda

The Great Bustard, the heaviest European bird, is found in parts of the large cultivated plains of central Europe, western Asia and north-west Africa. The male weighs up to 17 kg, the female 6 kg. Great Bustards make their nest in a depression in the ground. The female incubates the 2—3 eggs herself, and she also leads the young about, though they feed themselves from birth. Great Bustards feed mainly on plants, seeds and various invertebrates, occasionally also catching voles. In winter they roam over a wide area around their home.

283

Red-backed Shrike

Hoopoe

RED-BACKED SHRIKE
Lanius collurio

The Red-backed Shrike is a bird about 18 cm long, which builds its nest of roots and stalks in thorny bushes. When it has caught food, such as beetles, it often impales it on the thorns of a bush on the edge of woods or in a hedge, which it uses as its larder. The female incubates the 3—8 eggs mainly on her own, but both parents then feed the young on insects, their larvae and small vertebrates. The Red-backed Shrike is one of the most frequent foster-parents of cuckoos. In August it flies southwards to tropical and southern Africa, returning in the middle of May.

WHITE STORK
Ciconia ciconia

The White Stork, a wader about 1 m tall, lives in Europe and in Asia as far east as Japan. In winter, European storks fly as far as southern Africa, returning in the first half of April. They build their nests from sticks and branches in trees, on roofs or on tall chimneys. They constantly extend them, returning to the same one every year. Both parents take turns to incubate the 4—5 eggs, and they regurgitate food onto the nest for the young, then in two months the young storks begin to fly. Storks are exclusively carnivorous, hunting small vertebrates and invertebrates in fields, meadows and marshes and by the waterside.

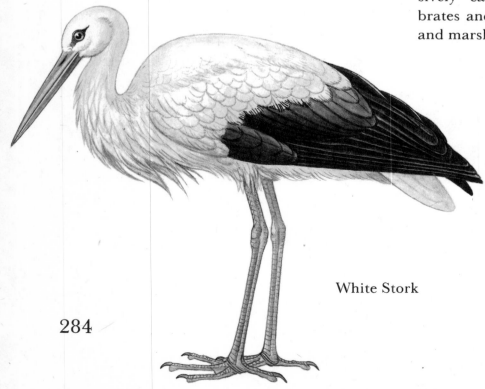
White Stork

Common Partridge

Common Quail

HOOPOE
Upupa epops

The Hoopoe is found almost throughout Europe, Asia and Africa, and is a migrant bird about 28 cm long. It leaves its European breeding ground for tropical Africa in September, returning in April. It lives in meadows and pastures close to water, in mature woodland and in sparse deciduous forests, where it makes its nest in a tree hollow or in a pile of stones. The female incubates her 6—7 eggs herself for 16—20 days, her mate feeding her throughout this period, then both parents feed the young. Hoopoes mainly eat insects and insect larvae, which they pull from the soft earth with their beaks or extract from cattle dung in pastures.

COMMON PARTRIDGE
Perdix perdix

The Common Partridge occurs in almost the whole of Europe and in central Asia. It is about 29 cm long, and lives in steppes, meadows, fields and plains. Partridges are resident, gathering in flocks in winter, and spending their whole life in the same pairs. In May or June the hen bird lays 8—24 eggs in a lined hollow in the ground, incubating them herself, while the cock bird keeps watch nearby. The parents share in caring for the young and leading them in search of food. Partridges feed on insects, worms, spiders, molluscs, seeds and green plants.

COMMON QUAIL
Coturnix coturnix

The Common Quail is a small bird which is native to Europe, Asia and Africa, and is about 17.5 cm long. In autumn Quail migrate from Europe to North Africa and Arabia, returning in flocks at the end of April to their homes in plains, fields and dry meadows.

Each cock Quail has several mates, each hen laying 6—18 eggs in a lined hollow in the ground, and taking sole charge of her chicks. Quail feed on insects and spiders, seeds and green plants.

Photograph by Oldřich Mazůrek

Czechoslovakia, country garden, "Bohemian Paradise" region

IN THE GARDEN AND NEAR PEOPLE

MAMMALS

HEDGEHOG
Erinaceus europaeus

The Hedgehog makes its home in parks, bushy gardens and deciduous woodlands. It is an insectivore about 30 cm long, with sharp spines covering its back; it rolls up into a prickly ball when in danger. Hedgehogs sleep through the day in piles of leaves or in holes, going out hunting after dark. They eat insects, earthworms, slugs, small vertebrates, birds' eggs and occasionally fallen fruit. They are not even afraid of the venomous adder, which they soon overcome and eat. The female makes a nest in a hole or among leaves in the bushes, where she gives birth to 3—8 young. These are blind, and have soft, light-coloured spines. They open their eyes after 2 weeks.

EUROPEAN MOLE
Talpa europaea

In gardens, parks, meadows and fields small heaps of newly-dug earth can often be seen. This is the work of the Mole, an insectivore about 16 cm long which is found in Europe and eastwards across the Caucasus to Lake Baikal in the USSR. The Mole works tirelessly, digging tunnels beneath the ground, where it lives and feeds on insects, insect larvae and earthworms. In a special chamber about 60 cm below the surface the female gives birth to 3—9 blind young, which open their eyes after 3 weeks.

EUROPEAN LONG-EARED BAT
Plecotus auritus

The European Long-eared Bat is commonly found near or in towns, villages and cities in Europe, Asia and North Africa. These bats sleep in roofs and outhouses during the day, setting out to hunt insects at twilight. In June the female gives birth to 1—2 young, which cling tightly to their mother's body. She suckles them for about 6 weeks, after which they become independent. Long-eared Bats hibernate during the winter in cellars, caves or disused mineshafts.

Hedgehog

European Mole

European Long-eared Bat

BLACK RAT
Rattus rattus

The Black Rat was originally a native of tropical Asia and Africa, but it spread over the world on board ships, although it has now disappeared again in many parts of Europe. Black Rats like to live in human dwellings and are often found in lofts, outbuildings and woodsheds. About 6 times a year females give birth to 4—20 hairless, blind young, which open their eyes after 2 weeks. Black Rats feed mainly on plant material and domestic rubbish.

BROWN RAT
Rattus norvegicus

The Brown Rat was carried throughout the world by ships coming from eastern Asia. This rodent is somewhat larger than the Black Rat, and likes to live near water, being a good swimmer and diver. Brown Rats are common in sewers, from which they get into cellars, storehouses and rubbish tips through wastepipes. They live in groups, making nests in burrows which they dig themselves. Females give birth to 6—22 blind young, up to 7 times a year; they open their eyes after 2 weeks. Brown Rats are omnivorous, eating grain and animal feed, green plants, small mammals and birds.

HOUSE MOUSE
Mus musculus

The House Mouse was probably originally native only to Asia Minor, but today it is

Black Rat

Brown Rat

House Mouse

found throughout the world. It inhabits villages and towns, where it lives beneath floors, in lofts, barns, sheds and holes in walls, and feeds on all kinds of food found in homes and warehouses. House Mice make their nests out of gnawed scraps of paper, rags, straw or hay in well-hidden places. Here the female gives birth to up to 12 young several times a year. These are blind at birth, opening their eyes after 12 days.

BEECH MARTEN
Martes foina

The Beech Marten is a carnivore about 75 cm long, including its tail. It inhabits rocky places and also lives near people in barns, sheds and the lofts of both inhabited and empty houses. Behind a wooden beam or in a woodpile the female makes a nest of leaves and grass where she gives birth to 3—7 young, which open their eyes after 34 days. Beech Martens go hunting after dark, catching mice, brown rats and small birds,

but occasionally also robbing henhouses or stealing ducks' eggs. In autumn they like to eat fruit, especially plums.

POLECAT
Putorius putorius

The Polecat occurs almost throughout the whole of Europe, but also in Asia and North America. It is a stoat-like carnivore about 60 cm long, including its tail. It lives in woods and fields, and it is commonly found close to human settlements, often making its home in a barn, haystack, woodshed, etc. From here Polecats make night-time forays into henhouses, where they may kill dozens of chickens in one night. Their main food consists of mice, brown rats, small birds, frogs and even fish. They are excellent swimmers, but poor tree-climbers. They make breeding nests of dry grass, where the females give birth to 3—11 young in April or May. These are blind, and open their eyes only after 30—37 days. When threat-

Beech Marten

Polecat

Weasel

Stoat

ened, for example by a dog or fox, the Pole-cat secretes an evil-smelling substance from glands beneath its tail to discourage its foe from pursuing it.

WEASEL
Mustela nivalis

The Weasel is a small carnivore found throughout Europe and in Asia and North America. It lives in fields and meadows and on the edge of forests, but often also in villages and towns. It moves close to human habitations especially in winter, in search of its main food, which is mice. Weasels also hunt young rats or ground-squirrels, and catch small birds. The female gives birth in

her den to 3—12 blind young, which open their eyes 3 weeks after birth.

STOAT
Mustela erminea

The Stoat is distributed throughout Europe. In winter its coat is a beautiful snow-white, only the tip of its tail remaining black, and this winter coat is known as ermine. Stoats like to live close to people, and they settle in holes in walls, in barns and in woodsheds, hunting mice, voles, small birds and insects. In April or May the female gives birth in her lair to 3—7 young, which open their eyes after 40 days.

BIRDS

JACKDAW
Corvus monedula

The Jackdaw, about 33 cm long, is found in the whole of Europe. It is a gregarious bird which lives in large flocks in winter, when they roam the countryside with Rooks, and

in the mating season. In March flocks of Jackdaws take up residence in ruined buildings, in towns, parks and woodland, or on cliffs and in quarries. Usually in May, individual pairs build their nests of twigs, moss and feathers in hollows. The 4—6 eggs are mainly incubated by the female, then both parents feed the young. Jackdaws feed on

Jackdaw

insects, spiders, worms, small vertebrates, seeds and berries.

COMMON STARLING
Sturnus vulgaris

Common Starlings can be found over the whole of Europe, and are 21.5 cm long. They have almost completely abandoned their original habitat in deciduous woodlands, moving to centres of population and often roosting in huge numbers in city centres. The female makes her nest of roots and dry grass between April and June, in holes in trees or in nesting boxes. For 2 weeks the parent birds take turns to incubate the 4—6 eggs, then they feed the young on insects, molluscs and earthworms, and after about 3 weeks the young fly. In winter Starlings migrate in huge flocks from northern

Common Starling

House Sparrow

Chaffinch

Europe to southern Europe or North Africa, though from western Europe they fly to the British Isles.

HOUSE SPARROW
Passer domesticus

The House Sparrow is the commonest bird of Europe and Asia, but it is also found in Africa, America and Australia. It is a resident bird, 14.5 cm long, and is found near humans, being widespread in villages, towns and cities. In March Sparrows begin to collect grass stalks, hay, scraps of paper and feathers in their beaks to build their nests. This is a spherical structure with a side entrance, placed in the branches of trees, often in bird-boxes, in the hollows of trees, in gut-

ters and similar spots. The female lays 3—8 eggs, which the parents take turns to sit on for 2 weeks. They also share in the feeding of the young. Sparrows' main food is seeds and green plants, and in summer they also eat insects.

CHAFFINCH
Fringilla coelebs

The Chaffinch, a 15-cm-long songbird, is found over a large part of Asia, throughout Europe, western Siberia and north-west Africa, and is very common in gardens, parks and well-illuminated woodlands. In early spring the female builds a nest jammed in the fork of a branch, using moss, lichen, cobwebs, and pieces of bark as cam-

293

Swallow

House Martin

ouflage. She incubates the 5 eggs herself, then both parents feed the young on insects and spiders. Adult birds live chiefly on seeds.

SWALLOW
Hirundo rustica

The Swallow is found all over Europe, Asia, North Africa and in North America. It was originally an inhabitant of rocky places, but now lives mainly in villages and towns, where conditions suit it better. European Swallows spend the winter in tropical Africa. They return to their homes at the beginning of April, moving into barns, sheds, stables and other outbuildings. They make a dish-shaped nest of balls of clay stuck together with saliva, using pieces of straw to reinforce it. In the nest bowl, lined with soft feathers, the female lays 5 eggs, which she incubates herself. Both parents feed the young on insects, which they catch in mid-air, then the young swallows fly after 20 days.

HOUSE MARTIN
Delichon urbica

The House Martin is native to the whole of Europe, and also lives in Asia and north-west Africa. Like the Swallow, it has made its home close to people. It flies to its European homes from the south in the second half of April. House Martins usually build their covered nests, with a side entrance, below the eaves of houses, several pairs often building close to each other. The nest is made of mud mixed with saliva. Both parents take turns to incubate the 5 eggs, and also share in feeding the young on mayflies and other flying insects, which they catch in the air. The young birds first fly 20 days after hatching, then in September or October flocks of House Martins leave for Africa.

294

Great Tit

GREAT TIT
Parus major

The Great Tit is found in gardens, parks and woods, and is a native of Europe, much of Asia and North Africa. Great Tits are resident. In spring they build their nests in holes in trees, in bird-boxes and various crevices, using moss, hair and feathers. The female sits on her 8—10 eggs for 2 weeks, while her mate supplies her with caterpillars and other insects, then the young are fed on insects, insect larvae and spiders by both the parents. In winter the Great Tit is a frequent visitor to bird tables, and likes eating fat and seeds, particularly sunflower seeds.

BLACKBIRD
Turdus merula

The Blackbird, originally an inhabitant of woodlands, has now settled close to human habitations, where it is very common. It is found in parks, gardens, bushy places and well-lit woods, and nests in bushes and low trees, on beams in sheds, window ledges and similar places. The nesting material used is stalks, roots, leaves and scraps of paper. Blackbirds nest twice yearly, or even more, and the female usually incubates her 4—6 eggs herself for 13—15 days. At the age of 2 weeks, the young jump down and hide on the ground, though they are still unable to fly. The parents feed them on earthworms, insects and molluscs. In autumn and winter Blackbirds feed mainly on berries, and often visit bird tables.

SONG THRUSH
Turdus philomelos

The Song Thrush is a summer migrant in most parts of eastern Europe, whilst in the west there are substantial resident populations. Song Thrushes live in parks, gardens

Blackbird

Song Thrush

Black Redstart

Common Swift

and woods, and half-way through April their nests of dry grass, leaves and moss, lined with mud, can be found in the bushes. The female incubates her 3—6 blue eggs with black spots for 12—14 days, and both parents feed their young. Song Thrushes eat worms, snails, insects and berries. They are well-known for their habit of smashing snails against stones in order to break the shells.

BLACK REDSTART
Phoenicurus ochruros

The Black Redstart arrives back from its winter home on the Mediterranean at the end of March. Originally found in rocky areas, it now lives near humans. It builds its nest of roots, straw and dry leaves in holes in walls, on window ledges and on rocks high in the mountains. The female usually lays 5 eggs, which she incubates herself,

then both parents feed the young on insects. In October Black Redstarts migrate southwards to warmer regions.

COMMON SWIFT
Apus apus

From half-way through May the piercing cry of the 16.5-cm-long Common Swift can be heard from the sky, when this bird returns from tropical Africa. Swifts are masterly and extremely fast fliers, catching insects in the air at a speed of up to 200 km per hour. Swifts are found in Europe, part of Asia and North Africa, and they spend most of their lives in the air. They have underdeveloped legs, and cannot take off from the ground. They nest in towns, on tall buildings and beneath the eaves and in roof-spaces of houses. They make their nests from feathers and pieces of straw which they manage to catch in the air, stick-

296

Barn Owl

Collared Dove

ing them together with saliva. The 2—3 eggs are incubated by the female, while the male brings her food, and the young are fed by both parents. At the beginning of August Swifts fly south again.

COLLARED DOVE
Streptopelia decaocto

The Collared Dove, about 28 cm long, was originally a native of southern Asia, but today has settled all over Europe. It is found in gardens, parks and among trees both in the country and in cities. It nests three times a year, building a nest of dry twigs in the branches of a tree. Both parents take turns to sit on the 2 eggs, which hatch in 14 days. 3 weeks later the young are led from the nest. Collared Doves feed on blackberries, seeds and molluscs and often fly to bird tables, where they eat a variety of scraps.

BARN OWL
Tyto alba

In Europe the Barn Owl, originally an inhabitant of rocky countryside, is now more usually found near human habitations, nesting in barns, derelict buildings, church towers or dovecotes. The female incubates her 4—6 eggs for about a month, while her mate provides her with food. The young, which usually leave the nest after 55 days, are looked after by both parents. The main food of the Barn Owl is mice and voles. This bird, which is about 34 cm long, is found on every continent.

Photograph by Ivo Petřík

Czechoslovakia, the High Tatras

ALPINE MARMOT
Marmota marmota

The Alpine Marmot, a rodent about 85 cm long with a bushy tail, is found in the Alps, the Carpathians in central Europe and the Tatras in Czechoslovakia and Poland. Marmots live in largish communities, digging deep burrows in the ground, often on a hard stone base, and the lair usually has several entrances. Here the female gives birth to 2—6 young, which open their eyes after 20 days. Marmots feed both by night and by day, eating grass, other herbaceous plants, seeds and various fruits. They warn each other of danger by means of shrill whistles, and hibernate from late September to April.

CHAMOIS
Rupicapra rupicapra

The Chamois, an inhabitant of mountain areas of Europe, reaches a height of about 75 cm at the shoulder and a weight of 40—60 kg. It climbs and jumps agilely over rocky mountain slopes, and lives in small herds, each led by an old and experienced male. For most of the year adult males live separately. Away from the herds, between April and June, females give birth to 1 or occasionally 2 or 3 young. Chamois feed on grass, other herbaceous plants and the leaves of bushes.

ALPINE IBEX
Capra ibex

The Alpine Ibex is found mainly in the Alps. Females, kids and young males wander in small herds, while old males form groups of their own. Males weigh up to 110 kg, but the females have smaller horns and weigh only about 50 kg. Ibexes frequent steep mountain slopes overgrown with grass, on which they graze from early morning. At midday they usually rest, but

Alpine Marmot

300

Chamois

Alpine Ibex

one of the herd keeps constant watch, warning the rest of approaching danger with a shrill whistle. Females usually have a single young, which follows its mother after only a few hours, and is immediately able to climb steep mountain slopes.

NUTCRACKER
Nucifraga caryocatactes

In Europe the Nutcracker is mainly found in coniferous forests in mountainous regions of southern Scandinavia, and in central and south-eastern regions. It is a large member of the crow family, 32 cm long. In harsh winters Siberian Nutcrackers sometimes fly south from the coniferous, evergreen forests of their native land. As early as March they build their nests of broken pieces of twigs in the dense branches of spruce trees, lining them with moss, hair and feathers. The female sits on the 3—4 eggs herself, and is fed by the male, then the young leave the nest after about 23 days. Nutcrackers feed on seeds, stone pine nuts, beechnuts and insects, sometimes varying their diet with the young of other species of birds.

RING OUSEL
Turdus torquatus

The Ring Ousel, a songbird about 24 cm long, with a white half-moon marking on its breast, is found in mountainous regions of Europe. It inhabits sparse mountain forests, and in northern Europe and the British Isles it is found in peat-bogs and near fast-flowing mountain streams. Ring Ousels build their nests of twigs, straw and moss in trees, or sometimes among stones on the ground. The female incubates the 4—6 eggs mainly on her own, and both parents feed the young. The diet of Ring Ousels consists mainly of insects and insect larvae, worms, small molluscs, and berries in autumn. They leave central Europe for the Mediterranean in the winter, returning in March.

WALL CREEPER
Tichodroma muraria

The Wall Creeper, about 17 cm long, is found in mountain regions such as the

Nutcracker

Ring Ousel

Wall Creeper

Pyrenees, the Alps and eastwards through the Balkans as far as the Himalayas. During the mating season Wall Creepers live in pairs, but otherwise they are solitary. Their nests of grass and moss are built in deep rock crevices, then in May the female lays 3—5 eggs, which she incubates herself for 18 days. The young are fed by both parents. Wall Creepers feed on insects and insect larvae and on spiders. In winter they fly down from the mountains to lower ground.

GOLDEN EAGLE
Aquila chrysaetos

Golden Eagle

The Golden Eagle is a huge bird of prey, reaching a length of 90 cm and a wingspan of 2 m, which occurs in large mountain areas of Europe. In March or April these eagles build their large nest of branches on a ledge, high on an inaccessible rock face. Here the female lays 1—2 eggs, and her mate takes occasional turns with their incubation. The young hatch after 45 days, and it is mainly the male eagle which hunts prey for them, while the female divides up the food, then after 70—80 days the eaglets fly. The prey of the Golden Eagle consists of birds and small mammals, and a female eagle, which usually weighs only about 4.5 kg, can take prey weighing up to 7 kg.

Rock Partridge

ROCK PARTRIDGE
Alectoris graeca

The Rock Partridge, a chicken-like bird about 35 cm long, is found in the Alps and other mountains of southern and south-eastern Europe, living in rocky places overgrown with grass and shrubs. Between April and June the female lays 9—15 eggs in a hollow lined with grass and leaves. She incubates the clutch herself, but the chicks, which find their own food, are led about by both parents.

Rock Partridges eat seeds, berries, green plants, and in summer also insects, molluscs and worms.

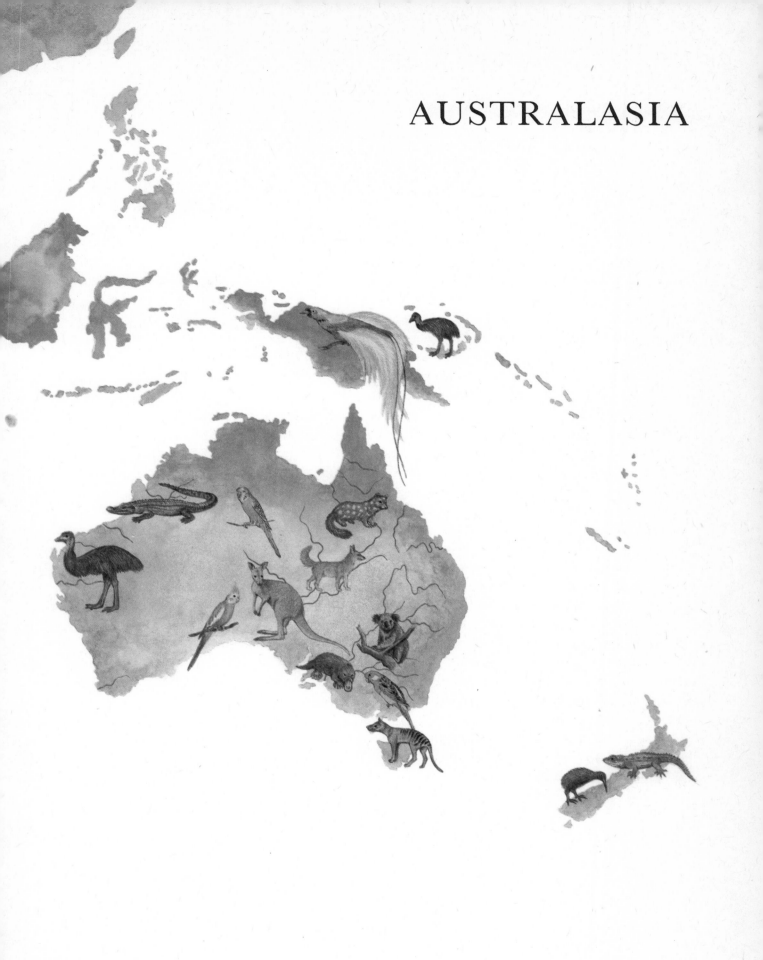

Australia, Tasmania, New Guinea, New Zealand and the neighbouring islands have their own flora and fauna, which cannot be found anywhere else in the world. For this reason they make up an independent region, known as **Australasia** or **Notogaea**.

Australia is the smallest of the continents. Its name comes from the Latin word *australis*, meaning southern. The countryside in Australia is mostly flat and the climate very dry, especially inland, where many of the large rivers and lakes dry up altogether in the dry season. In the north the climate is tropical to subtropical; in the south it is temperate.

A typical feature of the landscape is 'mulga', dense acacia scrub growing on arid tracts of land. Another type of landscape consists of areas covered with a number of different kinds of eucalyptus trees, all producing several thin trunks above a woody rootstock. This is known as 'mallee'. Along the northern and eastern coasts of Australia there are broad belts of forests. These are also found in the south-east and the south-west. In the north-east and to some extent also in the east of the continent there are rainforests. In the south the winters are quite cold and damp, while the summers are hot and dry; on higher ground in the south there are frequent winter snowfalls.

The first settlers in Australia, who probably came from south-east Asia, arrived there about 25 000 years ago. At the time the earth was going through an ice age, when the sea level was about 70 m lower than it is today. This increased the area of the islands and landmasses, reducing the distances between individual islands strung out between south-east Asia and the Australian coast. For this reason, people from south-east Asia were able to get to the Philippines, then to New Guinea and on to Australia, using only primitive boats.

However, Australian aborigines are not of one type, and settlement probably did not take place all at once. The members of some southern Australian tribes have light-brown skin and long hair, while in the north and on Tasmania there are aborigines with extremely dark skin and curly hair. Today those aborigines who live away from civilization still go about naked and barefoot, wearing only a hide belt to which they attach their game. They live just as they have done for thousands of years, hunting with spears and the boomerang. There are many types of boomerang, from heavy hunting ones which do not come back to lighter ones which, if they miss their target, return approximately to the place from which they were thrown. The aborigines seldom keep a fire going, and are adept at lighting one using a stick turned on a flat piece of wood.

Humans brought the domestic dog to Australia; many of these later became wild, giving rise to a new species of wild animal, the dingo.

The Australian fauna is remarkable; it took shape in the Tertiary era, when the Australian continent finally separated from the Asian landmass. While elsewhere in the world the original animals of the Tertiary era have been superseded by more advanced evolutionary forms, the monotremes (lowest order of mammals) and marsupials of that period have survived in Australia, including the duck-billed platypus, the spiny anteater, kangaroos, the koala bear and many others.

306

The Australian Forests

The typical Australian tree is the eucalyptus, growths of which make up over ninety per cent of Australian forests. Over five hundred species of it grow there, from stunted shrubs to huge trees reaching a height of over 100 m. These trees have a number of special features which are not found in other species. In the tropical belt of northern Australia they grow at temperatures around 50° C in the shade, while in the mountain regions of the Australian Alps they are not affected even by severe frosts.

The bark of some species of eucalyptus is constantly being shed. It contains a great deal of resin, which makes it burn very well. One spark is enough to set the bark alight, and the flames quickly spread until one tree after another catches fire and the whole forest becomes a roaring inferno. The animals that live there flee in panic as the fire advances. But before long the flames die down and incredibly the trees do not seem to suffer much damage. After the first rain new leaves sprout, and within a fortnight no one would know that a fire had been raging there.

Eucalyptus trees are a splendid sight when they are in flower, their crowns glowing with thousands of red, orange and yellow brush-shaped blossoms. There are over 500 species of Eucalyptus or gum tree, most of them natives of Australia or Tasmania.

The eucalyptus forests are the home of many species of arboreal marsupials, many of which, like the famous koala bear, feed exclusively on eucalyptus leaves. Some Australian marsupials are similar to European squirrels, while others are predatory.

Photograph by Stanislav Chvapil

The Australian Deserts and Bush

Large inland areas of western and central Australia consist of inhospitable desert. In some places these deserts are sandy, with an unusual red colour, in others clayey; but they are quite barren. It rains very little in these areas, and there are some particularly dry places where sometimes not a single drop of rain falls for several years running. Because of this, the Australian deserts are practically uninhabited. The few animals that do live there are those species which can obtain water either from plants or from other animals, such as insects, on which they feed.

The inland deserts are often bordered by grassy, treeless plains, with only occasional patches of bushes. Most of the vegetation consists of drought-resistant Spinifex grasses, whose spiny leaves make travelling through them very unpleasant.

Large expanses of the Australian bush are made up of the two characteristic types of bushland, 'mulga' with its acacia bushes and 'mallee' with eucalyptus.

Photograph by Stanislav Chvapil

The Australian Waters and Swamps

There is very little fresh water in Australia. In the tropical areas there are broad rivers near the coast, but they are very short and are fed with water only during the rainy season. The longest river is the Murray-Darling, rising in Queensland and flowing into the Indian Ocean near Adelaide in South Australia.

In West and South Australia there are a number of lakes, the largest of which is Lake Eyre. Most of these, however, are also full only in the rainy season, and only the largest have water in them all the year round. For this reason thousands of birds migrate from inland areas to spend the dry season on the coast.

River banks near the sea and deltas, particularly in tropical regions, form extensive swamps in some places, thickly overgrown with various species of mangrove. The surfaces of lagoons and creeks are covered by water-lilies with huge, beautiful, light-blue flowers. There are many rare species of fish and other animals in the rivers of Australia.

Photograph by Stanislav Chvapil

New Guinea

After Greenland, New Guinea is the largest island in the world. It is surrounded by thousands of smaller islands and islets, many of which are of volcanic origin, while others are coral atolls. The west half of New Guinea is Irian Jaya and the east half is Papua New Guinea.

The New Guinean climate is a tropical one. There are high mountains on the island, with active volcanoes. There is plentiful rainfall the whole year round, and the mountain regions are constantly wet. Fast brooks and streams run down the mountain slopes, often forming waterfalls.

New Guinea has extensive rainforests, with a huge number of plant species. Trees grow to a height of about 90 m, and their crowns are a blaze of colour with the flowers of innumerable orchids. While the island's flora is more like that of south-west Asia, the fauna is mostly closely related to that of Australia. Typical birds of New Guinea are the world-famous birds of paradise.

The original inhabitants of New Guinea are the Papuans, who live in the south-eastern part of the island and who were cannibals until recently.

Today Papuan people decorate a special room kept for the 'initiated' with the skulls and bones of tree kangaroos; not so long ago the decoration would have been of human skulls and bones.

Photograph by Bedřich Forman

New Zealand

The New Zealand archipelago consists of the large North and South Islands and a number of smaller ones. The climate of North Island is subtropical; on South Island it is temperate. The almost 4 000-m-high Southern Alps stretch almost the whole length of South Island, their peaks covered with snow all year, and in places there are glaciers. There are also many large lakes on South Island.

Large complexes of deciduous forests grow in New Zealand, providing valuable wood for the manufacture of furniture and other items.

The fauna of the country is peculiar. One remarkable bird is the flightless kiwi. On some of the small islands there can be found the only surviving member of a group of reptiles common in the Mesozoic era, the tuatara.

The huge flightless moa was almost entirely wiped out by humans in the 14th century. The largest species, the giant moa, grew to a height of 3.6 m, and its eggs were over 25 cm long. The main cause of the extinction of this bird was the coming of the Maoris, who settled in New Zealand from eastern Polynesia half-way through the 14th century. But even before that, moas had been hunted by seafarers who visited the islands in their primitive craft. It has now been scientifically proved that some species of moa survived on the South Island until about three hundred years ago.

Photograph by Vladimír Šibrava

AUSTRALASIA

AUSTRALIA

MAMMALS

Bear, Koala

Cat, Tiger

Dingo

Kangaroo, Red

Numbat

Platypus, Duck-billed
Possum, Greater Gliding

Quokka

Tasmanian Devil

Wolf, Marsupial
Wombat, Common

BIRDS

Budgerigar

Cockatiel
Cockatoo, Red-tailed
Cockatoo, Roseate or Gallah

Eagle, Wedge-tailed
Emu

Fowl, Mallee

Gallah or Roseate Cockatoo
Goose, Cape Barren
Goose, Pied

Kookaburra, Laughing

Lyrebird, Superb

Parrot, Australian King
Penguin, Little Blue

Rosella, Eastern

Swan, Black

Turkey, Brush

Wren, Splendid

REPTILES

Crocodile, Saltwater

Taipan

AMPHIBIANS

Treefrog, Green

INVERTEBRATES

Spider, Funnel-web

Termite, Compass

NEW GUINEA

MAMMALS

Kangaroo, Matschie's Tree

BIRDS

Bird of Paradise, Black Sickle-billed
Bird of Paradise, Blue
Bird of Paradise, Greater
Bird of Paradise, King
Bird of Paradise, Superb
Bird of Paradise, Twelve-wired
Bowerbird, Golden
Bowerbird, Striped

Cassowary, Bennett's

NEW ZEALAND

BIRDS

Kakapo
Kea
Kiwi, Brown

Parakeet, Red-fronted

Shelduck, Paradise

Takahe

REPTILES

Tuatara

Photograph by Stanislav Chvapil

Subtropical bush — Hattah National Park, Victoria

THE
AUSTRALIAN
FORESTS

MAMMALS

KOALA BEAR
Phascolarctos cinereus

The Koala Bear is not really a bear at all, even though it is a popular children's teddy bear. In fact it is a marsupial, weighing up to 15 kg. It feeds only on the leaves of a few species of eucalyptus trees, but eats only the mature leaves, since the young ones poison it. It spends almost its whole life in the treetops, and sleeps in the daytime, crawling about the branches after dark. A single male usually has several mates. In June the female gives birth to a single young, which spends the first half year of its life in its mother's pouch. After leaving the pouch it spends another year with its mother, who carries it first on her stomach, then on her back.

GREATER GLIDING POSSUM
Schoinobates volans

The Greater Gliding Possum lives in the broad eucalyptus forests of eastern Australia. It is a marsupial about 90 cm long, though more than half of this is its bushy tail. Along the sides of its body from its front to its back legs it has a broad flap of skin. When it stretches out its limbs these flaps are like wings, which it uses to glide through the air for a distance of up to

Koala Bear

Numbat

Greater Gliding Possum

a hundred metres, steering itself with its tail. During the day the possum hides in tree hollows, where it makes a nest out of leaves. This herbivore goes in search of food after sunset, mainly eating the buds, shoots and flowers of eucalyptus trees.

NUMBAT
Myrmecobius fasciatus

The Numbat is a predatory Australian marsupial with a body about 25 cm long and an 18-cm-long tail. It does not attack vertebrates, however, and is quite harmless. Its only food is termites and ants and it catches these on its long tongue, which it can thrust out to a distance of up to 15 cm, after having torn apart the termites' nest with its sharp claws. Numbats live in sparse eucalyptus forests, and hunt during the day. The female has no pouch, and the young hold on very tightly to her teats. There are usually 4 young, and they are difficult to see in the mother's long body hair.

MARSUPIAL WOLF
Thylacinus cynocephalus

By the time European settlers arrived in Australia, the Marsupial Wolf was to be found only in Tasmania. But it has now probably disappeared even from there, since none has been sighted since 1938. It was the largest of the predatory marsupials, almost 70 cm tall. It lived in grassy and bushy savannahs, where it hunted young kangaroos and other marsupials, birds and lizards. The female carried her 2—4 cubs for 3 months in a flat pouch with its opening facing backwards. When they were older she would leave them in a lined den.

TIGER CAT
Dasyurops maculatus

The Tiger Cat is about 100 cm long, and its home is in forest areas of eastern Australia and Tasmania. It is a predatory marsupial cat, which hunts at night. It catches small kangaroos, rabbits and lizards, and in the

Marsupial Wolf

Tiger Cat

trees it also seeks out birds and their eggs. It often visits henhouses to steal poultry. The female has 4—6 young, which she carries in her pouch for a long time, then when they are older she carries them on her back.

BIRDS

BRUSH TURKEY
Alectura lathami

The Brush Turkey, which is about 70 cm long, inhabits rainforests and bushy areas, particularly in north-eastern and eastern coastal areas of Australia. The male, which has massive legs, spends several months scraping together a large heap of vegetable material and earth from a wide area, and he builds this up to 1.5 m high. When the temperature of the rotting pile reaches 33° C, the female begins to lay her eggs, which she places in holes scraped in the heap. She then carefully looks after the eggs in their 'incubator', regulating their temperature by adding or taking away the material which covers them. In 2 months the young hatch,

Brush Turkey

and are independent at once. Brush Turkeys feed on worms, insects, molluscs, seeds, berries and green shoots.

RED-TAILED COCKATOO
Calyptorhynchus magnificus

The Red-tailed Cockatoo is a parrot up to 60 cm long, distributed through western, northern and eastern Australia. Outside the breeding season these birds live in large flocks in the treetops, feeding on various fruits, nuts, seeds and shoots. During the breeding season they live in pairs, nesting in the hollows of trees. The female lays a single egg, which she incubates herself for 30 days, then both parents feed the young. They leave the nest after about 9 weeks.

AUSTRALIAN KING PARROT
Alisterus scapularis

The Australian King Parrot occurs in eastern Australia and southwards as far as southern Victoria. It grows to a length of 43 cm. It has a forest habitat, but outside the

Red-tailed Cockatoo

breeding season flocks of these parrots also fly into town parks and gardens. During the breeding season they live in pairs. They nest in hollows in the trunks of trees, usually near the crown. The female lays 3—6 eggs

Australian King Parrot

Eastern Rosella

319

and incubates them herself, while her mate feeds her. The young, which leave the nest after 5 weeks, are fed by both parents. King Parrots feed on seeds, fruit and shoots.

EASTERN ROSELLA
Platycercus eximius

The Eastern Rosella, a 30-cm-long member of the parrot family, occurs in eastern and south-eastern Australia and Tasmania. It was originally an inhabitant of savannah woodlands, but in many places, such as Sydney and Canberra, it has taken up residence in city parks. From these the birds make regular trips to the surrounding fields in search of grain. They also eat various seeds, green shoots, berries, fruit and the nectar of flowers; sometimes also insects. In a tree hollow the female lays 4—9 eggs, which she incubates herself, while the male feeds her several times a day. Both parents feed the young.

LAUGHING KOOKABURRA
Dacelo gigas

The Laughing Kookaburra, some 46 cm long, lives in forests and bushy areas in south-eastern Australia. It hunts insects and small vertebrates, and beats small snakes or lizards to death, using its powerful beak. It feeds its young on the same diet. Laughing Kookaburras nest in tree hollows, where the female lays 3—4 eggs. The young hatch after 24 days, and both their parents tear up large prey for them. These birds have a very loud voice, rather like a mocking laugh.

Laughing Kookaburra

Superb Lyrebird

SUPERB LYREBIRD
Menura novaehollandiae

The Superb Lyrebird is a strange bird living in the thick forests on the coast of south-eastern Australia. The male reaches a length of up to 130 cm, but a full 70 cm of this is made up of its exquisite decorative tail feathers. During the mating season a male usually has several females. The female builds a large roofed-over nest from twigs, rootlets and moss on a rocky ledge or in thick undergrowth at the base of a tree. She incubates the single egg and feeds the young by herself. After 6 weeks the young leave the nest. Lyrebirds feed mainly on insects, worms and molluscs, using their strong legs to dig them out of the ground or from piles of leaves.

AMPHIBIANS

GREEN TREEFROG
Hyla caerulea

The Green Treefrog has a body up to 12 cm long. It lives in northern and eastern regions of Australia and New Guinea, and is found in forests and city parks. During the day these treefrogs hide in a damp spot among the thick leaves of bushes or trees. After sunset they catch insects, spiders and centipedes, geckos and the young of small species of birds. During the mating season they seek out swamps and peat-bogs.

Green Treefrog

Photograph by Stanislav Chvapil

Semidesert to desert landscape in the subtropics — Victoria

THE AUSTRALIAN DESERTS AND BUSH

MAMMALS

DINGO
Canis dingo

The Dingo is not one of the original inhabitants of Australia. It is a descendant of the domestic dog taken there by man long ago from South-east Asia. In Australia the Dingo became wild, and over thousands of years turned into a new form of canine carnivore. Family groups or small packs of them are found in broad expanses of bushland or in sparse woodlands. They hunt and attack their prey in packs. Their favourite victims are kangaroos, but they also often kill wandering sheep. They also eat agamas, monitors and snakes. Under an overhanging bank, the dingo bitch gives birth to 3—7 blind pups, which open their eyes after about 10 days.

TASMANIAN DEVIL
Sarcophilus harrisi

The Tasmanian Devil is a predatory marsupial with a huge, striking head, and is about the size of a cocker spaniel. It was originally found throughout Australia, but today it occurs only in bushy and rocky tracts of Tasmania. On the mainland the Dingo has replaced its marsupial counterpart. The Tasmanian Devil is exclusively carnivorous. It hunts small kangaroos, birds and reptiles, but also feeds on carcasses. It eats smaller prey whole. The female has 3—4 young, which she carries in her pouch. They leave the pouch after 15 weeks, when the mother puts them in a den in a hollow tree, visiting them regularly to suckle them.

COMMON WOMBAT
Vombatus ursinus

The Common Wombat, a marsupial about 1 m long, inhabits mountain forests and rocky places in Tasmania and south-eastern

Dingo

Tasmanian Devil

Australia. During the day wombats sleep in shallow burrows, which they dig with their sharp claws. After dark they set out in search of food. They feed on grass, roots from bushes and the fine bark of trees. The female has a single young, which develops inside her pouch.

RED KANGAROO
Macropus rufus

The Red Kangaroo is the largest of the Australian kangaroos. An adult male is the height of a human when it is sitting, and weighs around 150 kg. The female is about one third smaller. Red Kangaroos live in large herds on open grassy plains and bushy areas. The herd is led by a huge male. During the day these kangaroos take cover in the bushes, usually searching for food only after sunset. They eat grass and other herbaceous plants, and browse on the leaves of bushes. When they have eaten their fill, they rest lying on their sides, though some constantly stand guard.

The female gives birth to a tiny, naked young, only 3 cm long, with undeveloped eyes and ears. Using the claws on its front

Common Wombat

Red Kangaroo

legs it finds its way by instinct into its mother's pouch, where it holds on tight to her teat. The baby kangaroo puts its head out of the pouch for the first time to look around it only after about 150 days. It is another 50 days before it leaves the pouch to move about on the ground close to its mother, but if danger threatens it leaps straight back in. At the age of 250 days it finally leaves the pouch.

BIRDS

EMU
Dromaius novaehollandiae

The Emu is one of the most famous Australian birds, and has found its way into the national coat of arms. It reaches a height of 1.5 m and a weight of about 50 kg, and lives in bushy areas and sparse forests. At the start of the Australian winter the female lays 10—12 dark green eggs in a shallow depression lined with leaves and grass. The male incubates the eggs, sitting

Emu

Cape Barren Goose

on them for 8 weeks, and the father also takes the young to feed and looks after them. The Emu's main food is seeds, grass, leaves, berries, flowers and insects, and during the dry season flocks of Emus migrate to better feeding grounds. They are unable to fly, but can run at a speed of about 40 km per hour.

CAPE BARREN GOOSE
Cereopsis novaehollandiae

The Cape Barren Goose, which is about the size of the domestic goose, lives on the small islands along the southern coast of Australia. After the nesting season it flies to the mainland. These birds live permanently in pairs, and during nesting individual pairs each defend a territory. The female lays her 3—6 eggs in a hollow lined with grass, and incubates them herself while her mate keeps

Wedge-tailed Eagle

watch near by, driving off intruders. The black and white striped young are led about by both parents. These geese feed on grass and other vegetation, and partly also on seeds.

WEDGE-TAILED EAGLE
Aquila audax

The Wedge-tailed Eagle, a bird of prey with a wingspan of about 2.5 m, occurs throughout Australia and Tasmania and in the south of New Guinea. It is common in the plains, in bushy areas, and in sparse forests. In a tall tree pairs of these eagles build a nest of branches, which they line with green leaves. Both parents take turns to sit on the eggs, and both feed the young. They mainly eat the flesh of dead animals, but also hunt small reptiles and birds. Only rarely do they attack a small kangaroo or lamb.

MALLEE FOWL
Leipoa ocellata

The Mallee Fowl is a chicken-like bird about 60 cm long which is found in eucalyptus groves in the dry regions of central Australia. During the winter the male laboriously builds a large pile of sand and forest debris. In it the female lays 14—20 eggs,

Mallee Fowl

Galah or Roseate Cockatoo

Cockatiel

which are warmed by the heat of the decomposing vegetable matter. The male checks the temperature regularly with his sensitive tongue. The young hatch gradually after 52—60 days, and are able to fend for themselves immediately after hatching. Mallee Fowl feed on worms, insects, molluscs, seeds, berries and green leaves.

GALAH or ROSEATE COCKATOO
Eolophus roseicapillus

The Galah, or Roseate Cockatoo, is a very common parrot, found almost throughout Australia and Tasmania. Outside the mating season Galahs roam about in large flocks, which stay together even during the nesting period. Individual pairs nest in the hollows of dead trees. The female lays 2—5 eggs on a lining consisting of a few leaves. Both parents take turns to incubate the eggs, and both also feed the young. The fledglings leave the nest at the age of 6 weeks. Galahs eat seeds, shoots and fruit, and sometimes also insects.

COCKATIEL
Nymphicus hollandicus

The Cockatiel, a parrot about 32 cm long, occurs over almost the whole of Australia, moving from place to place to find food. Its main habitat is in the bush and in sparse woodlands. Pairs of Cockatiels make their nests in hollows in the branches of trees. Both parents share in incubating the 5—7 eggs, and both feed the young, which leave the nest after about 4 weeks. The Cockatiel's diet consists mainly of grass seed, and also of cereal grains from the fields, the nectar of eucalyptus flowers, green shoots, and sometimes also insects.

Budgerigar

Splendid Wren

BUDGERIGAR
Melopsittacus undulatus

Budgerigars are found almost everywhere in Australia. This member of the parrot family is about 18 cm long, and the male has blue nostrils, the female brown. Budgerigars in the wild are mostly green in colour. Outside the mating season they roam the countryside in enormous flocks, looking for areas where there are plenty of grass seeds, which form their diet. Even during nesting individual pairs of birds stay close to the others. The female lays her 3—6 eggs in a hollow in the trunk or branch of a tree, and incubates them herself. Both parents feed the young, which fly from the nest after 30—35 days. Budgerigars are very popular cage birds.

SPLENDID WREN
Malurus splendens

The Splendid Wren, which is about 14 cm long, inhabits bushy areas in the mountainous regions of the southern half of Australia. These birds are very tame, and pairs of them often make their home close to human dwellings. They build a spherical nest of straw, with an entrance at the side. Females usually lay 3 eggs, incubating them alone. Both parents feed the young, mainly on insects and spiders.

Taipan

REPTILES

TAIPAN
Oxyuranus scutellatus

The Taipan is one of the most venomous snakes in the world, reaching a length of up to 4 m. It inhabits Queensland and southern New Guinea. The venom glands of adult specimens contain enough venom to kill as many as 80 people. The Taipan lives in bushy areas and catches small birds and mammals for food. The female lays eggs, from which the young snakes hatch after 3 months.

INVERTEBRATES

FUNNEL-WEB SPIDER
Atrax robustus

The Funnel-web Spider, whose body is up to 2 cm long, is found in coastal regions of eastern Australia. It is one of the most venomous spiders in the world, and its bite may be fatal to humans. The spider's name comes from the funnel-shaped web which it builds on the ground, and in which it catches insects. It lies in wait for them in a tunnel which it also spins.

COMPASS TERMITE
Amitermes meridionalis

The Compass Termite is found mainly in northern Australia. It builds a mound-like nest up to 5 m tall from masticated plants, dung and earth. This nest always points north to south, with its broader sides facing east to west. Because of this, it is used as a compass by aborigines and travellers. Over a million insects may live in one of these termite colonies. Compass termites feed on the roots of bushes and on all types of wood, often destroying telegraph poles or even wooden buildings.

Funnel-web Spider

Compass Termite

Photograph by Stanislav Chvapil

Tropical swamp in Queensland, near Cairns

THE
AUSTRALIAN
WATERS
AND
SWAMPS

MAMMALS

DUCK-BILLED PLATYPUS
Ornithorhynchus anatinus

The Duck-billed Platypus, about 40 cm long, is one of a very few species of mammals which lay eggs. It is found in small lakes, rivers and large streams in south-eastern Australia and in Tasmania. In the water it catches the larvae of insects and crustaceans, and in the mud picks out worms and molluscs. It hunts both by day and by night, and eats its own weight in food — about 0.75 kg — every day. Platypuses dig burrows several metres long in banks. In a nest lined with eucalyptus leaves and grass the female lays 1—3 eggs, which she incubates for about a week. The young, which open their eyes after 18 days, feed on their mother's milk, which they suck from glands on her belly.

QUOKKA
Setonix brachyurus

The Quokka is an inhabitant of swampy districts and small damp forests in the southern coastal area of Western Australia. This small species of kangaroo feeds on grass, shoots and the leaves of bushes, setting out to feed after dark. The female carries the young in her pouch for 6 months.

Quokka

Duck-billed Platypus

BIRDS

LITTLE BLUE PENGUIN
Eudyptula minor

The Little Blue Penguin is only 40 cm tall. Its home is on the small islands off the south-eastern and south-western coasts of Australia and New Zealand, where it is found only close to the coast, since it hunts for food in the sea. These penguins feed at night, catching small fish, molluscs and crustaceans. They keep together in large communities, and individual pairs build themselves nests in holes in the ground, or in rock crevices, lining them with grass and seaweed. The female lays 2 eggs, sharing the incubation of them with her mate. Both parents also feed the young.

PIED GOOSE
Anseranas semipalmata

The Pied Goose measures up to 90 cm in length, and is found in tropical regions of northern Australia and in the south of New Guinea. Pied Geese gather in flocks on lagoons or shallow creeks, where they feed on seeds and swamp vegetation. A male often has two mates, and the trio work together to build a large nest of plants in a shallow part of the water. Both the females lay their eggs in the same nest, and the young are led about by both mothers and the father.

BLACK SWAN
Cygnus atratus

The Black Swan, 130 cm long, is found on lakes, lagoons and watercourses throughout the southern half of Australia and north-eastern Queensland. It builds a nest of twigs, grass, leaves and aquatic plants on a small island or on flattened reeds. The female lays 3—9 eggs, sharing the incuba-

Pied Goose

Little Blue Penguin

Black Swan

tion with her partner. Both parents also lead and protect the cygnets. Black Swans feed mainly on aquatic plants, but also eat grass and seeds on the bank.

REPTILES

SALTWATER CROCODILE
Crocodylus porosus

The Saltwater Crocodile occurs from the north coast of Australia, through Indonesia to southern India, being found in estuaries and even far out at sea. It occasionally grows to more than 8 m in length, but most specimens are about 4 m long. This huge reptile is very aggressive, and will readily attack people. Saltwater Crocodiles eat all animals which they are capable of overcoming, dragging them under the water until they drown. The female buries 25—60 eggs in the earth by the waterside, then piles up a heap of leaves and mud, which may be 90 cm high, in order to warm them. The mother then guards her 'incubator' until the young hatch, which takes 2—3 months.

Saltwater Crocodile

Photograph by Bedřich Forman

Coast of West Irian

MAMMALS

MATSCHIE'S TREE KANGAROO
Dendrolagus matschiei

The home of Matschie's Tree Kangaroo is the forested areas of New Guinea. This marsupial, which is 140 cm long, including its 60-cm-tail, is a skilful tree climber. Its long front legs with strong claws are well-adapted for climbing, while its hind legs are shorter. Tree Kangaroos feed on shoots, leaves, and also berries and fruit, which they tear from the trees with their front legs. The female has a single young, which she carries in her pouch for several months.

Matschie's Tree Kangaroo

Bennett's Cassowary

BIRDS

BENNETT'S CASSOWARY
Casuarius bennetti

Bennet's Cassowary, a large flightless bird weighing up to 50 kg and 80 cm tall to its back, is an inhabitant of the north-west of New Guinea. It lives in thick undergrowth, where it moves about adroitly, and it is also a good swimmer. It feeds mainly on fallen fruit, seeds, leaves and insects. The female lays 8 eggs, in a depression lined with leaves and grass. They are incubated by the male, who also takes charge of the young.

STRIPED BOWERBIRD
Amblyornis subalaris

The Striped Bowerbird is found in the mountain forests of south-western New

339

Golden Bowerbird

Striped Bowerbird

Guinea. It grows to a length of about 26 cm. During the breeding season the male makes himself a sort of arbour round the trunk of a tree. This is made from orchid stems, and has two entrances. Around the arbour he makes a round garden of moss, to which he carries large numbers of black sticks, berries, and the black wing-cases of insects. He then entices the female into this decorated bower. The male does not take part in the actual business of nesting: the female builds her own nest in a tree, lays 2 eggs in it, and incubates them herself. She also feeds the young herself. Bowerbirds feed mainly on soft berries and fruit.

GOLDEN BOWERBIRD
Sericulus aureus

The 28-cm-long Golden Bowerbird is distributed in southern, western and north-western New Guinea, where it lives on wooded mountain slopes. In the breeding season the male builds a large structure of twigs and sticks, consisting of two opposite walls joined by a horizontal stick which is white with lichen. He also places white lichen on the floor between the walls and in front of the entrance, and decorates the walls with white flowers. In this way he entices the female. She then builds a nest of twigs in a tree, where she lays and incubates her 2 eggs. She also feeds the young herself. Golden Bowerbirds feed mainly on soft berries.

GREATER BIRD OF PARADISE
Paradisaea apoda

The Greater Bird of Paradise is found mainly on the islands of Aru and Misool, near New Guinea. The male reaches a length of up to 1 m, but 70 cm of this is taken up by his ornamental tail feathers. Greater Birds of Paradise live in the tops of the tallest trees, where they find their food — soft fruit, berries and insects. During the mating season the males of the area gather

Greater Bird of Paradise

together and jump about on the branches of trees, displaying their splendid tail feathers. But they take no part in nesting. The females build nests of twigs and leaves, where they incubate their 2 eggs. They also feed the young themselves.

BLUE BIRD OF PARADISE
Paradisaea rudolphi

The Blue Bird of Paradise is found in the woodlands of hilly areas in eastern and south-eastern New Guinea. It lives in the treetops. Including his beautiful long tail feathers, the male reaches a length of over 90 cm. Each male has his own place on a thin branch, from which he removes the leaves. Here he makes his courtship display, frequently hanging head-down and spread-

Blue Bird of Paradise

341

Superb Bird of Paradise

ing his blue tail-feathers and wings out wide. The female then builds a nest of twigs, incubating her 2 eggs herself. She also feeds the young herself, on fruit, berries and insects.

BLACK SICKLE-BILLED BIRD OF PARADISE
Epimachus fastuosus

The Black Sickle-billed Bird of Paradise lives in the mountain forests of western and central New Guinea. It seeks its food in the tallest treetops, mainly eating soft fruit, berries and insects. During the mating season males grow two tail feathers up to 85 cm long. At this time these elegant birds attract the females by displaying the feathers of their tails and flanks, and opening their sickle-shaped bills wide to show the bright greenish-yellow lining. The female builds her nest of twigs and leaves in the bushes, quite close to the ground. She incubates her

Black Sickle-billed Bird of Paradise

2 eggs herself, and also feeds the young on her own, with insects and fruit.

SUPERB BIRD OF PARADISE
Lophorina superba

The Superb Bird of Paradise is distributed almost throughout the thick mountain for-

342

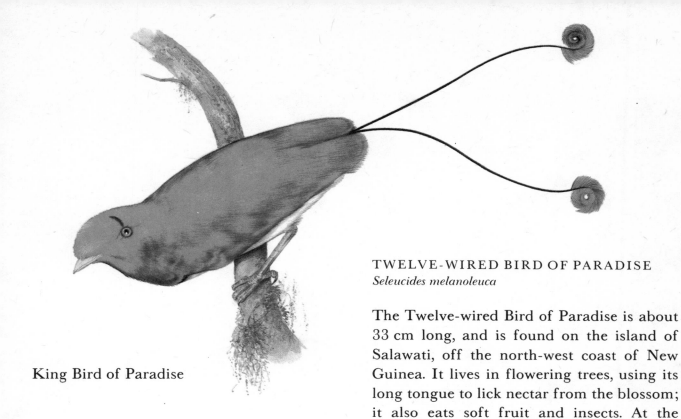

King Bird of Paradise

TWELVE-WIRED BIRD OF PARADISE
Seleucides melanoleuca

The Twelve-wired Bird of Paradise is about 33 cm long, and is found on the island of Salawati, off the north-west coast of New Guinea. It lives in flowering trees, using its long tongue to lick nectar from the blossom; it also eats soft fruit and insects. At the mating season males grow twelve long tail feathers which look like bent wires. The female is entirely responsible for nesting and the care of the offspring.

ests of New Guinea. It feeds on berries, fruit and small invertebrates. The male sits on a branch stripped of leaves and spreads his shining breast feathers, while the female looks on from a short distance away. She incubates the eggs and feeds the young on her own.

KING BIRD OF PARADISE
Cicinnurus regius

The King Bird of Paradise occurs in the thick mountain jungles of New Guinea and on the nearby islands, including Aru and Misool. It lives in the crowns of trees, where it eats soft fruit and catches insects. It reaches a length of 22 cm, and in the mating season the male grows two long tail feathers with coloured 'discs' on the ends. The female makes her nest in a hollow left in a tree by woodpeckers, lining it with leaves and moss. She incubates the eggs and feeds the young herself.

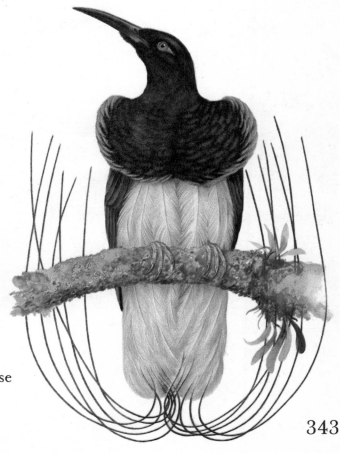

Twelve-wired Bird of Paradise

343

Photograph by Vladimír Šibrava

Akaroa, South Island

NEW
ZEALAND

BIRDS

BROWN KIWI
Apterix australis

The Brown Kiwi is a flightless bird native to New Zealand. It is 55 cm long, weighs 3 kg, and is a nocturnal creature, leaving its shelter to search for food only after nightfall. It thrusts its long beak into the ground and picks out worms, molluscs and insects. Kiwis live in pairs throughout the year, and use their strong legs to dig a burrow, or make their home in a hollow in the ground. Here the female usually lays 1 egg, but sometimes as many as 3. They are incubated by the male. For the first 5 days the young are sustained by their yolk sacs, after which they set off with their father to hunt for food.

KEA
Nestor notabilis

The Kea, a large parrot about 50 cm long, is found in New Zealand, in the Alps on South Island, where it lives on bush-covered slopes at the upper edges of the forests. It digs tunnels up to 3 m long in the ground, and the nest is made in a hollow in the rocks. The female lays 2—4 eggs, sharing their incubation with her mate, and both parents also feed the young. Keas feed mainly on seeds, berries, roots and green plant materi-

Brown Kiwi

Kea

Kakapo

Red-fronted Parakeet

al, but also eat worms, insect larvae, and even the flesh of dead mammals and various scraps from people's kitchens. In some areas they have even been known to attack lambs and young sheep, tearing the flesh from their backs with their beaks. For this reason farmers have almost eradicated this species.

KAKAPO
Strigops habroptilus

The Kakapo is an inhabitant of New Zealand, and is about 60 cm long. It does not fly, but climbs deftly about the trees, occasionally gliding down from them for a distance of 20—30 metres. This nocturnal bird, sometimes called the Night Parrot, spends the day in a tree hollow close to the ground. After dark it picks berries, shoots and blossoms, sometimes also eating insects or other invertebrates. These birds are mostly found in forests, usually near water. They make their grass and feather nests in holes in the ground, and the female lays 2—3 eggs, which she incubates herself.

RED-FRONTED PARAKEET
Cyanoramphus novaezelandiae

The Red-fronted Parakeet, a member of the parrot family which is about 27 cm long, is distributed in the forests of New Zealand and the nearby islands. Outside the mating season these birds wander about in small flocks, then during the nesting season they form pairs, making their nests in tree hollows or rock fissures. The female lays 5—9 eggs, which she incubates herself, then both parents feed the young.

PARADISE SHELDUCK
Tadorna variegata

The Paradise Shelduck is found on the lakes and rivers of New Zealand. The male has a jet-black head, while the female's is snow-white. These birds like to nest in the hollows of old trees, usually 3—8 m above the

347

Paradise Shelduck

Takahe

ground. The female sits on her 6—11 eggs herself, while her mate keeps watch nearby. As soon as the newly-hatched young have dried, they jump down to the ground and their parents lead them to the water. Paradise Shelduck feed on grass, various other green plants and seeds; in summer they also eat invertebrates.

thick grass on the ground, and the female incubates her 2 eggs on her own. During the first few days after the young are born the parents bring food for them in their beaks. Takahes eat seeds and green plant material, the young also feeding on insects, spiders and worms.

TAKAHE
Notornis mantelli

The Takahe, which is about 50 cm long, lives in New Zealand; previously it was distributed throughout the whole of South Island, but today it is very rare. It nests in

REPTILES

TUATARA
Sphenodon punctatus

Today the Tuatara is found only on a few small islands off the coast of New Zealand.

Tuatara

This rare lizard grows to a length of up to 75 cm. It digs holes in the ground, but often takes up residence in the burrows of petrels. Tuataras leave their lairs at night to hunt insects, molluscs and worms. The female lays her eggs in a shallow pit dug near the burrow, and the young take a full year to hatch. Tuataras grow very slowly and live to a ripe old age. They were once common in New Zealand, but the dogs, cats and rats imported by Europeans have almost wiped out this lizard.

THE OCEANS,

SEAS AND POLES

Oceans and **seas** cover seventy per cent of the surface of the earth, and have a great influence on the climate of the various continents. The seas are joined to each other, and many sea creatures migrate regularly through the endless oceans, just as birds migrate through the air. Cetaceans, for example, and many marine fish, travel frequently from northern seas to the south, and vice versa.

The waters of the oceans and seas are constantly in motion. Along regular 'rivers', huge marine currents roll through the oceans, some warm, others cold. The warm Gulf Stream, for example, washes the shores of western Europe, making the weather there warmer, while the cold Peruvian Stream has a cooling effect on the climate of the Pacific coast of South America.

The greatest effect on the surface marine currents is exerted by the wind. Some winds blow across the oceans in the same direction the whole year round. Deep-sea currents occur through the differing temperatures of water layers near the surface and deep down. The gravitational pull of the sun and the moon cause regular tides to ebb and flow in the seas. Waves break constantly against the shore, seething across the sand or thumping against the rocks.

The Earth has two poles, the **North Pole** and the **South Pole.** Both of these are very cold regions. The northern polar region comprises the Arctic Ocean, with an area of some 13 million km² and up to 5 180 m deep, and the northernmost tips of the continents of Asia, Europe and America, along with their offshore islands. The total area of the Arctic region is around 25 million km².

While in the Arctic there is no land at all for a long way around the pole, the South Pole lies in the continent of Antarctica, which has an area of more than 13 million km². The total area including islands and shelf ice is actually about a million square kilometres larger still. Antarctica has the greatest average height above sea level of all the continents, about 2 000 m, though this of course includes the ice-cap.

The continent is divided into east and west Antarctica, according to the type of terrain. East Antarctica is entirely covered by the ice-cap, while west Antarctica has mountains rising above the ice. The highest of these is the Sentinel ridge, reaching a height of 5 140 m, the highest point in Antarctica. But only 0.3 per cent of the continent has no ice cover. The total volume of the Antarctic ice is 24 million cubic kilometres, which constitutes about 90 per cent of all the world's drinking water.

There are at present dozens of scientific expeditions working at permanent research stations in Antarctica. Experts have already detected large mineral deposits there, including coal, iron ore, lead, silver, gold, uranium and other useful minerals. But their recovery from under the immensely thick layer of ice remains a problem.

The Arctic Polar Region

There is no land at the North Pole. The surface of the Arctic Ocean is covered all the year round by a thick layer of ice, the extent of which changes during the year. In summer huge blocks of ice break off the edges of the ice-cap and drift southwards. The enormous icebergs, most of whose bulk is under the water, gradually thaw during their journey, until they finally melt altogether in the warmer seas further from the Pole.

The most northerly parts of three continents reach into the arctic region — North America, Europe and Asia. The largest island in the world — Greenland — and many smaller islands are also situated in the Arctic.

The North Polar region is very cold, and for most of the year has heavy frosts. In spite of this the Arctic is inhabited by many animals which are adapted to the harsh life in the far north. All the mammals which live in this region have thick fur and a deep layer of subcutaneous fat.

The land areas of the Arctic are covered by treeless tundra, overgrown with lichens, grass and dwarf shrubs, which grow close to the ground. During the northern summer the tundra blossoms for a short time with countless lovely arctic flowers, although only the upper layers of the ground thaw out even in summer. The lower levels remain permanently frozen, and this 'permafrost' prevents the surface water from draining away. Because of this there are thousands of large and small lakes in the tundra during the summer season, when water and marsh birds nest there.

There are also human inhabitants of the Arctic, tribes which made their home in this inhospitable northern landscape many thousands of years ago.

The most northerly regions of Europe and Asia are inhabited by Lapps, Yakuts and Tungus — nomadic peoples who migrate annually with their herds of half-wild reindeer to find food for their animals. The arctic areas of North America and Greenland are the home of the Eskimos, who are mainly hunters and fishers.

Photograph by Josef Tomas

Antarctica

Around the South Pole stretches the antarctic landmass, which covers an area larger than that of Europe. Antarctica has the coldest climate on earth, and the world's lowest recorded temperature was measured there — minus 88.3° C. It is coldest inland, where the temperature only rises to minus 20° C even on the warmest days. Most of the continent is covered by a huge mass of snow and ice throughout the year, and the ice-cap is more than 4 km thick in places.

No creature can live permanently at such low temperatures. The only inhabitants of Antarctica today are human beings, who work there temporarily in scientific stations. However, within a distance of 300 km of the Pole the first living organisms are found. Growths of moss and lichen appear on bare rock surfaces during the summer months.

The coast of Antarctica and the offshore islands have a much warmer climate than the interior. In summer there is no snow, and the temperature at ground level is between 15° and 20° C. During this season some low vegetation even flowers. In the winter months of July and August, large snowfalls occur here, and the sea is covered with ice up to a distance of 100 m from the shore. Frequent and strong blizzards form huge snowdrifts. But even in this season the antarctic landscape is not entirely lifeless. Large flocks of antarctic penguins winter there, and even lay and hatch their eggs in the intense cold. When winter has passed, thousands of other birds migrate to the islands and coast of Antarctica, where they nest and rear their young. The surrounding seas are a rich source of food in summertime.

Various forms of Pinnipedia — seals, sea-lions and sea-elephants — swim to the coast of Antarctica, where they give birth to their young. They are followed by large shoals of predatory cetaceans, the killer-whales. Men, too, come here to hunt — whalers and fur-trappers.

Photograph by Josef Sekyra

The Sea

The sea is where life originated three thousand million years or more ago, and where it underwent its early development. Every drop of sea water gives life to tiny single-cell animals and plants. There are incredible numbers of them — a single cubic metre of sea water contains up to a hundred thousand.

Various marine animals deposit eggs, spawn and larvae, which, together with other invertebrate forms — molluscs, crustaceans and worms — and small vertebrates, drifting or floating freely in the sea, make up what is called marine plankton. Plankton provides food for most of the marine animals, such as fish, which in turn fall prey to large, predatory creatures. Some sea animals even feed on the carcasses of their fellows, so nothing is wasted in the oceans.

Countless shoals of fish use the same routes year after year to migrate, either in search of food, or to reach the places where they spawn. They are followed by marine predators and fish-eating birds. In areas where fish gather during the birds' mating season, birds form large nesting colonies where they rear their young.

There is animal life from the surface of the ocean to its depths. In many of the shallow tropical seas, over millions of years, corals have built up large coral reefs and islands, called atolls. Sponges, sea-anemones and innumerable molluscs live on these. On the underwater rocks and the sandy seabed there are marine crustaceans, worms and echinoderms. The depths of the oceans, where there is constant darkness, are the home of the giant squid and luminescent deep-sea fish.

In various environments, marine animals form peculiar animal communities. Some live only in water at a certain temperature, others only at a certain depth, while still others inhabit the rocks along the surf-line or make their home on the sandy seabed.

Sea water contains an average of approximately 3.5 per cent of various salts, mainly sodium chloride or common salt.

Photograph by Jiří Felix

THE OCEANS, SEAS AND POLES

THE ARCTIC POLAR REGION

MAMMALS

Bear, Polar

Fox, Arctic

Hare, Blue

Lemming, Collared

Narwhal

Ox, Musk

Reindeer

Sable

Walrus
Wolverine

BIRDS

Buzzard, Rough-legged

Diver, Black-throated

Eider, King

Grouse, Willow

Jaeger, Pomarine

Smew
Swan, Bewick's

ANTARCTICA

MAMMALS

Seal, Crabeater
Seal, Leopard

Seal, Southern Elephant
Seal, Weddell's

Whale, Blue
Whale, Finback
Whale, Humpback
Whale, Ice Baleen
Whale, Killer
Whale, North Atlantic Pilot
Whale, Sperm

BIRDS

Cormorant, Blue-eyed

Gull, Kelp

Penguin, Adelie
Penguin, Emperor
Penguin, Gentoo
Penguin, King
Penguin, Macaroni
Petrel, Snow
Pigeon, Cape

Skua, MacCormick's
Sheathbill, Black-faced

Tern, Antarctic

THE SEA

MAMMALS

Dolphin, Bottle-nosed
Dugong

Manatee, North American
Manatee, West African

Otter, Sea

Seal, Common
Sea Lion, Californian

BIRDS

Booby, Peruvian

Cormorant, Guanay

Eider, Common

Frigatebird, Magnificent

Guillemot, Common

Pelican, Brown
Penguin, Black-footed
Puffin, Common

Tern, Inca
Tropicbird, Red-billed

REPTILES

Iguana, Marine

Krait, Yellow-lipped Sea

Snake, Yellow-bellied Sea

Turtle, Green
Turtle, Hawksbill
Turtle, Leatherback

FISH

Anglerfish

Dogfish, Lesser Spotted

Mackerel, Atlantic

INVERTEBRATES

Barnacle, Common Goose

Crab, Hermit

Lobster, Common

Oyster, Common European

South-western Greenland, northern part of Ikatoq Fiord

THE
ARCTIC
POLAR
REGION

———

MAMMALS

BLUE HARE
Lepus timidus

The Blue Hare lives in the cold northern regions of Europe, but is also found in the mountains of Scotland and in the Alps. It weighs up to 5.8 kg. In summer its coat is a rusty brown colour, but in winter its fur becomes white, serving as camouflage in the snow-covered landscape. Blue Hares are inhabitants of forests and tundra, sometimes wandering as far as the coasts. In a shallow depression beneath a bush, the female gives birth to 5—8 young up to three times a year; they are sighted at birth, and run about immediately.

COLLARED LEMMING
Dicrostonyx hudsonius

The Collared Lemming is a common rodent in the arctic regions, especially the tundras of Alaska and northern Canada. In summer it is brown, but is has a pure white coat in winter. Regularly every fourth year lemmings reproduce in unbelievable numbers, and millions of them set off on the long journey to find food. They are nocturnal, feeding on grass, leaves and the bark of bushes. They build their nests of grass and leaves just below ground level. Females give birth to up to 12 young, often three times a year.

POLAR BEAR
Thalarctos maritimus

The Polar Bear is a huge carnivore, in exceptional cases reaching a weight of 700 kg. It occurs in the Arctic, on the northern coasts of Norway, Greenland, North America and Asia, and usually lives on icebergs. Polar Bears can swim for a long time, but very slowly, and they do not dive well. For this reason they mainly hunt seals, which they attack on icebergs or on the shore. In the water they are unable to catch this agile prey. They also eat dead fish and other dead animals, and in summer feed on berries on the shore.

In a den dug in the snow the female gives birth, in November or December, to 2—3 young, which open their eyes after 4 weeks. Only in spring does the mother lead her cubs out and teach them to hunt.

Collared Lemming

Blue Hare

Polar Bear

WOLVERINE
Gulo gulo

The Wolverine is a carnivore some 50 cm tall and weighing about 30 kg. It lives in the forests of the far north of Asia, Europe and North America. Wolverines, also known as Gluttons, are not choosy about their food. They hunt small mammals and birds, but also eat eggs, carcasses, insects, worms and berries. However, only in times of shortage do they dare to attack young reindeer or moose. During the migration of the salmon to northern rivers Wolverines become en-thusiastic fishers. The female gives birth in her lair to 2—4 young, which open their eyes after 4 weeks.

SABLE
Martes zibellina

The Sable, a northern member of the weasel family, has fine, valuable fur. It occurs in the coniferous forests of northern and eastern Siberia, and is about 45 cm long, about 15 cm of which is its tail. It is an excellent climber, and hunts squirrels and small birds

Wolverine

Sable

in the trees. For most of the year it is solitary. It usually makes its lair in the hollow of a tree. Here the female gives birth to 3—4 young, which open their eyes after about 1 month.

ARCTIC FOX
Alopex lagopus

The Arctic Fox, about 30 cm tall and weighing 4.5—8 kg, inhabits the tundras of northern Asia, Europe and North America. It occurs in two forms — the more common white and the rarer blue. Arctic Foxes live in small groups. They often dig burrows to sleep in, though they may also sleep on the ground among stones. They are fast runners, climb well, and are good swimmers. They hunt both by day and by night. Their most common prey is lemmings, particular-

Arctic Fox

Walrus

ly when the latter reproduce in large numbers. They also feed on birds' eggs and on marine animals washed ashore by the tide, and berries in summer. In June the female gives birth to 6—12 young.

WALRUS
Odobenus rosmarus

The home of the Walrus is in the arctic regions around Greenland, Hudson Bay in North America and the coast of northern Asia, though it sometimes wanders as far as the north coast of Norway. The male reaches a length of 4.5 m and a weight of 2 200 kg; the female is much smaller with smaller tusks.

Walruses mostly live in pairs, which gather together in large herds. Their main diet consists of marine molluscs, crustaceans and fish, and they sometimes attack the young of seals. Walruses can stay underwater for 10 minutes, and dive to a depth of more than 30 m. The female has a single young, which is suckled for 2 years.

NARWHAL
Monodon monoceros

The Narwhal is a whale which lives in the Arctic Ocean. The male can reach a length of 6 m and a weight of 1 000 kg, while the female is smaller. Male Narwhals have a conspicuous tooth, up to 3 m long and curving to the left, projecting from their jaws. They use this tusk in fights with each other; females do not have a tusk. Narwhals usually live in small communities. They can dive to a depth of 400 m, and can stay under water for up to 30 minutes. They feed mainly on molluscs and crustaceans, and the female produces a single young.

Narwhal

363

Musk Ox

MUSK OX
Ovibos moschatus

The Musk Ox was at one time far more common in the Arctic than it is today. It is now found in the extreme north of Canada, Alaska and Greenland, and has recently been introduced into Norway and Spitsbergen. It lives in small herds in the tundra. The male reaches a height of 165 cm and a weight of up to 400 kg, while the female is smaller. Musk Oxen are herbivorous. At the beginning of May the female gives birth to a single calf, which frisks about its mother within an hour of birth.

REINDEER
Rangifer tarandus

The Reindeer, sometimes known as the Caribou, is found in the extreme north of Europe, Asia and North America. The male is larger than the female, and reaches a weight of 150 kg. Both male and female have antlers. Reindeer live in the tundras and northern woodlands as well as in the mountains of the north. European Reindeer are domesticated, but American Reindeer roam in the wild. Their main food is lichens, but

Reindeer

they also eat grass and leaves. Every year Reindeer make long trips in large herds to find new sources of food, moving northwards in spring and back to the south in autumn. In spring the female gives birth usually to a single young, though occasionally to 2—3.

BIRDS

BLACK-THROATED DIVER
Gavia arctica

The Black-throated Diver lives in northern Europe and the north-west of Asia, and also nests in Scotland. It is a water bird some 70 cm long, which during the mating season is found on lakes, usually near the coast. It builds its large nest in grass by the waterside, but always close to the surface of the water. The female lays 1—3 eggs, which the parents take turns to incubate. They lead the young to the water immediately after they hatch. In winter Black-throated Divers stay close to the coast of the Baltic and the North Sea. They feed mainly on fish, crustaceans, molluscs, worms and aquatic insects.

POMARINE JAEGER
Stercorarius pomarinus

The Pomarine Jaeger, about 52 cm long, is found in the arctic tundras of Asia and North America. It lives on lakes and slow-moving rivers, where it catches fish, molluscs and crustaceans. It often takes eggs from other birds' nests, or robs seagulls of their prey. Pomarine Jaegers build their nests on the ground in tufts of grass, and both parents take turns to sit on the 2—3 eggs. They both also feed the young.

KING EIDER
Somateria spectabilis

The home of the King Eider is on the coasts of northern Asia, North America and Greenland. This bird is about 56 cm long,

Black-throated Diver

Pomarine Jaeger

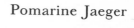

King Eider

Smew

and in the mating season the male is particularly strikingly coloured. In June the female lines a depression in the ground with plants and sticks, and lays 3—7 eggs. She surrounds the clutch with large amounts of fine down from her breast to protect the eggs from the cold. She sits on the eggs herself, and when the ducklings hatch out she leads them to the sea. King Eiders feed mainly on molluscs, insects, sea-urchins, small crustaceans and small fish. They sometimes also collect seeds from the shore.

SMEW
Mergus albellus

The Smew, a duck some 40 cm long, is distributed throughout the coniferous forests of northern Asia, being found near lakes and rivers. In a tree hollow the female lays 6—11 eggs, which she incubates herself. When the newly-hatched young have dried, they jump down from the nest and follow their mother to the water. In winter these ducks migrate to more southerly regions. They eat insects, molluscs, crustaceans, worms and small fish.

BEWICK'S SWAN
Cygnus bewickii

Bewick's Swan is an inhabitant of the coast and islands of northern Asia. It flies to its nesting grounds in the swampy tundras in April. The female builds her nest on raised ground close to water, using lichens, moss,

Willow Grouse

Bewick's Swan

grass and sticks and finally lining it with down. She sits on the 2—3 eggs herself, but both parents lead the goslings about. Bewick's Swans have a diet of grass, seeds, berries, and to a smaller extent also aquatic insects and crustaceans.

ROUGH-LEGGED BUZZARD
Buteo lagopus

The Rough-legged Buzzard is found throughout the arctic regions of Europe, Asia and North America. It reaches a length of 60 cm, and has a wingspan of 140 cm. This hawk has characteristically feathered legs and a conspicuous dark spot on each wing which shows when the bird is in flight. Each pair has its own hunting territory. The birds build their nest on the ground, in a low tree or on a rock overhang, from branches, bilberry plants and lichen. Usually at the beginning of June, the female lays 2—7 eggs, and incubates them herself. The number of eggs depends on the availability of small rodents within the territory. The male brings prey for the young, which his mate takes from him and gives to them. During nesting Rough-legged Buzzards feed mainly on lemmings. In winter they migrate to warmer regions, where they hunt for voles and other small mammals in the fields.

WILLOW GROUSE
Lagopus lagopus

The Willow Grouse occurs throughout the tundras of the Northern Hemisphere, and is

Rough-legged Buzzard

also found in Scotland and Ireland. In winter these birds are white all over except for their tails, though these are also covered over by white feathers. In spring the female makes a nesting depression in the ground, lining it with straw and leaves; in it she lays 5—12 eggs. Soon after they hatch the young leave the nest and their mother takes them to find food. Willow Grouse feed on willow catkins, green plant material, flowers, berries and seeds, and young birds also eat insects and insect larvae.

ANTARCTICA

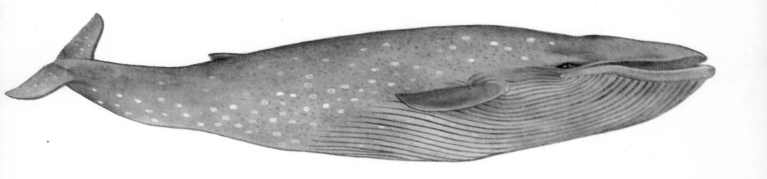

Photograph by Josef Sekyra

Queen Maud's Land, high-mountain region of Wohlhat Massif

LEOPARD SEAL
Hydrurga leptonyx

The Leopard Seal, also known as the Sea Leopard, is a huge pinniped, up to 3.5 m long and weighing up to 400 kg. It lives in the waters of Antarctica, especially in the Ross Sea, staying close to the shore, where it preys on penguins. But it also hunts squid and fish, and sometimes catches the young of other species of seals. On a rocky islet the female gives birth to a single pup about 70 cm long.

WEDDELL'S SEAL
Leptonychotes weddelli

Weddell's Seal lives in the waters of Antarctic where it likes to rest on icebergs. It grows to a length of about 3 m and a weight of up to 450 kg, and feeds mainly on fish and squid. In the summer the female gives birth to a pup up to 1 m long, which for the first week lies on the ice beside its mother. It then spends several weeks with her in the shallows close to the shore before going out to sea.

Leopard Seal

Weddell's Seal

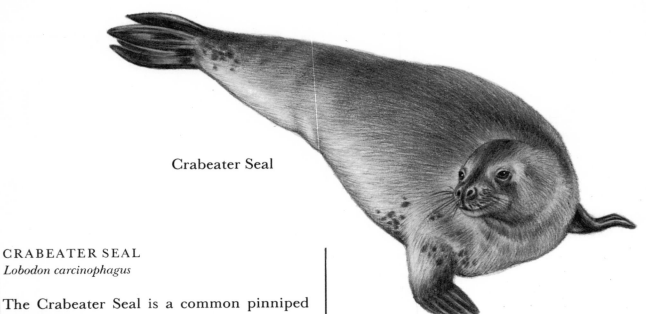

Crabeater Seal

CRABEATER SEAL
Lobodon carcinophagus

The Crabeater Seal is a common pinniped in Antarctic waters. In the winter months large herds of them swim as far as the shores of South America and Australia. In the second half of October the female gives birth to a single pup, usually on the bare ice. During this period these seals usually live in pairs. Crabeater Seals mainly eat marine crustaceans, which they find in the water with the help of their long, sensitive whiskers.

SOUTHERN ELEPHANT SEAL
Mirounga leonina

The Southern Elephant Seal is found in the warmer regions of the whole of Antarctica, and is particularly common on the islands of Kerguelen and South Georgia. An adult male grows to a length of 6 m and may

Southern Elephant Seal

Blue Whale

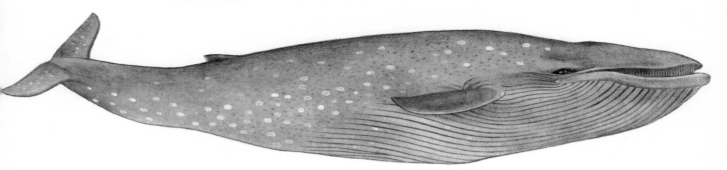

weigh as much as 4 000 kg, while the female is 3.5 m long and weighs up to 900 kg. These seals spend the winter on the open sea, then at the beginning of September large herds of them swim to the islands. A single male usually gathers 10—30 females around him, and each female gives birth to just one pup. Elephant Seals feed on fish and squids. They dive to a depth of up to more than 400 m.

BLUE WHALE
Balaenoptera musculus

The Blue Whale is the largest animal in the world. The longest ever caught measured 33.27 m, and most specimens weigh around 135 tonnes, as much as 25 adult elephants. Blue Whales feed almost entirely on krill. In winter they keep to warmer seas, and when the Antarctic spring comes they move to the colder waters of Antarctica, where there is plenty of food at that season. Females usually give birth to a single calf, weighing about 2 tonnes.

FINBACK WHALE
Balaenoptera physalus

The Finback Whale reaches a body length of 25 m and a weight of about 50 tonnes. These whales live in large groups, called schools. The calves are born in warmer seas, but afterwards Finback Whales move to Antarctic waters, where there are plenty of crustaceans. These form their main food, though they sometimes eat small fish swimming in large shoals near the surface.

Finback Whale

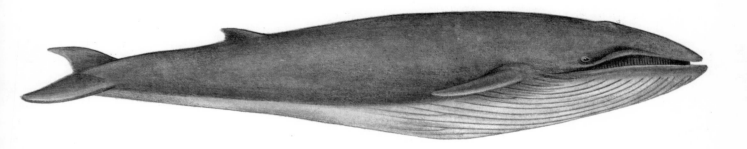

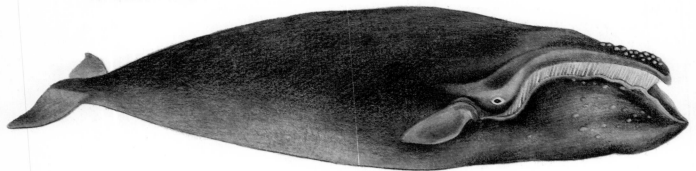

ICE BALEEN WHALE
Eubalaena australis

The Ice Baleen Whale has a conspicuously large head, and reaches a length of 23 m. It has unusually large jaws, with jawbones up to 4.5 m long, which are excellent for catching small marine crustaceans. These whales are distributed along the edge of the Antarctic region. The female produces a single calf, about 3.5 m long, which is suckled for a whole year. Ice Baleen Whales feed on plankton.

HUMPBACK WHALE
Megaptera novaeangliae

The Humpback Whale is a strange species, growing to a length of 18 m and a weight of around 33 tonnes. It swims very slowly, and so was easy to catch for the old whalers, even with a primitive harpoon. Humpback Whales travel great distances, appearing in winter around the equator and leaving for Antarctica in spring. They feed on small crustaceans. The female produces a calf 4 m long, which she suckles for 11 months.

SPERM WHALE
Physeter macrocephalus

The Sperm Whale is a huge toothed whale which reaches a length of 18 m and a weight of 50 tonnes. Females are only half the size of males, and stay in warmer seas the whole year round. In summer, large numbers of males swim to the waters of Antarctica. Sperm Whales usually hunt squids at depths of 500—600 m, but they also catch giant octopus and squids, with

Humpback Whale

Sperm Whale

which they sometimes fight fiercely in the depths. Females usually give birth to a single calf, 4 m long and weighing 1 300 kg.

KILLER WHALE
Orcinus orca

The Killer Whale, a large toothed cetacean, is one of the fiercest predators on Earth. Males can reach a length of 10 m, females up to 6 m. Killer Whales live and hunt in packs and even attack other large whales, tearing chunks of flesh from their bodies. They prey mainly on the young of other whales, but they also attack seals and penguins, and catch fish and squids. When pursuing their victims they swim at speeds of 37 km per hour or more. The female produces a single calf, 2 m long.

NORTH ATLANTIC PILOT WHALE
Globicephala melaena

The North Atlantic Pilot Whale is to be found in the seas at both the North and South Poles. Males grow to a length of 5 m, females to 4 m. In summer large numbers of these whales swim into Antarctic waters, where they feed mainly on squids and small fish.
Each male has several mates. Females give birth to a single young, 2.5 m long, which is suckled for up to 16 months.

North Atlantic Pilot Whale

Killer Whale

EMPEROR PENGUIN
Aptenodytes forsteri

The Emperor Penguin is a typical inhabitant of Antarctica. It nests during the worst of the Antarctic frosts when the temperature falls to as low as minus 60° C. It is the largest of the penguins, reaching a height of 122 cm and a weight of up to 46 kg. Emperor Penguins live in large colonies. The female lays a single egg, which she gives to her mate, who carefully rolls it with his beak onto his feet where it is covered by a fold of abdominal skin. The female sets off at once for the open sea, while the male stands still for a full 64 days incubating the egg. During all this time he eats nothing. When the young is born, its mother returns from the sea and brings it fish, crustaceans and small squids in her crop. Then the male, who has lost a great deal of weight during his 2-month fast, goes off to feed.

KING PENGUIN
Aptenodytes patagonica

The King Penguin is found in the warmer waters of the Antarctic seas. It reaches a height of 90 — 110 cm and a weight of 21 kg. King Penguins live in large colonies on the shores of islands, from where they go hunting in the sea. They eat fish, squids and crustaceans. In November or December the female lays a single egg, which she gives to her mate to look after; he warms it, pressed on top of his feet by a fold of skin on his belly, for 14 days. Then the female takes over for 4 — 5 days, and the two parents take

Emperor Penguin

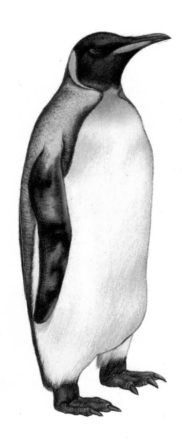

King Penguin

turns throughout the 54 days it takes the egg to hatch. Both parents feed the young penguin.

ADELIE PENGUIN
Pygoscelis adeliae

The Adelie Penguin lives mainly along the west coast of the Antarctic Peninsula and on the adjacent islands. It lives in large colonies, which may be several hundred thousand strong, and can reach a weight of 5—6 kg. At the start of the Antarctic summer, half way through October, the birds seek nesting places on rocks which are not covered with snow. In the first half of November the female lays 2—3 eggs, which the parents take turns to incubate for several days at a time. After 34 days the young hatch and their parents feed them on fish, squids and krill.

GENTOO PENGUIN
Pygoscelis papua

The Gentoo Penguin nests on the Antarctic Peninsula and the surrounding islands, growing to a weight of 5—8 kg. The birds build their nests in rocky places, lining them with blades of grass, pieces of bone and small stones. The 2 eggs are incubated by the male for the first 2—3 weeks, then the female takes over. The young hatch after 35 days, and their parents feed them on fish, small crabs and krill.

MACARONI PENGUIN
Eudyptes chrysolophus

The Macaroni Penguin lives mainly on the islands of Kerguelen, South Georgia, the South Orkneys, and in the warmer parts of Antarctica. It grows to a weight of about

Adelie Penguin

Gentoo Penguin

Macaroni Penguin

Blue-eyed Cormorant

4 kg. These birds build their nests on steep, rocky slopes overgrown with grass. The female lays 2 eggs, which both parents take turns to incubate, and both of them also feed the young on small fish.

BLUE-EYED CORMORANT
Phalacrocorax atriceps

The Blue-eyed Cormorant is distributed from the Antarctic Peninsula, northwards to the Falkland Islands and the south coast of South America. It lives in small colonies. The birds build their nest, of vegetable remains and feathers, on a rock overhang. For 32 days both parents share in the incubation of the 2—6 eggs. They then bring the young food four times daily — small fish, crustaceans and squids. These cormorants hunt their prey underwater, to a depth of up to 20 m.

CAPE PIGEON
Daption capensis

The Cape Pigeon nests mainly on the islands close to the Antarctic coast, but also in New Zealand and along the coast of southern Africa. This pigeon gathers in communities of up to several hundred birds. The female lays a single egg in a nest on a cliff and both parents take turns to sit on it, for 45 days, and both also look after the young, which they feed for 7 weeks. Cape Pigeons feed on krill, squids and small fish, which they catch on the surface.

SNOW PETREL
Pagodroma nivea

The Snow Petrel lives in Antarctic regions which are covered with ice and snow for most of the year. It is a small bird, growing to a weight of 500 g. Snow Petrels are

378

Cape Pigeon

Snow Petrel

among the best fliers, and can easily fly up to 300 km from their nesting place across the open sea. They live in small flocks. Both parents take turns to sit on the single egg, which the female lays on a rocky overhang. These birds feed on krill, squids and small fish, which they catch among the icefloes.

MACCORMICK'S SKUA
Stercorarius maccormicki

MacCormick's Skua nests on the Antarctic Peninsula and the islands to the north of it. Each pair has a large territory during the mating season. In a shallow depression, lined with pieces of bone and feathers, both parents take turns to sit on the 2 eggs. But in most cases only one young is reared, which they feed on the nest for 7 weeks on crabs, squids, fish, and the young and eggs of other birds. After nesting the birds roam the southern seas.

MacCormick's Skua

Kelp Gull

Antarctic Tern

KELP GULL
Larus dominicanus

The Kelp Gull is the only species of seagull nesting in the Antarctic region. It also occurs, however, in New Zealand and on the coast of southern Africa and South America. It lives in colonies, though often in pairs in Antarctica. These gulls build their nests of pieces of bone, grass and moss among the rocks. The female lays 2—3 eggs, which she and her mate take turns to sit on. They also both feed the young. This gull feeds mainly on crabs, squids and small fish, but they sometimes also eat the flesh of dead whales. Occasionally they eat the eggs or young of other birds.

ANTARCTIC TERN
Sterna vittata

The Antarctic Tern nests in small colonies in rocky places on the Antarctic Peninsula, building their nests in hollows on a dry gravel beach. The female lays 2—3 eggs, which both parents incubate alternately for 3 weeks. They then bring food for the young for 1 month. Antarctic Terns feed on small fish, crustaceans and molluscs, catching their prey on the surface of the water by flying along with their open beaks just submerged.

BLACK-FACED SHEATHBILL
Chionis minor

The Black-faced Sheathbill, over 40 cm long, is one of the typical inhabitants of the Antarctic region. Pairs of these birds build their nests in a fissure in the rocks or the abandoned burrow of petrels. The female lays 2—3 eggs, which both parents take regular turns to incubate. After the young have been reared, sheathbill families form flocks and move northwards. These birds are omnivorous, eating both vegetable and animal material. They often steal penguin eggs, sometimes even making off with the unguarded young, and also like to eat the carcasses of seals.

Black-faced Sheathbill

THE
SEA

Photograph by Jiří Felix

Caribbean Sea — coast of Cuba

Sea Otter

SEA OTTER
Enhydra lutris

The Sea Otter is 1.5 m long complete with its tail, and weighs up to 40 kg. It is an inhabitant of the coastal waters of North America from California to Alaska, and of the coast of north-east Asia. It is very well adapted for a marine life, and can dive to a depth of 50 m. On the seabed Sea Otters mainly catch sea-urchins, which make up sixty per cent of their diet. They also eat crustaceans, molluscs and fish. The Sea Otter is a diurnal creature, usually sleeping on a rocky islet at night. Here too the female gives birth to a single pup, which is hairy from birth and can see immediately. Its mother teaches it to swim right from the start.

CALIFORNIAN SEA LION
Zalophus californianus

The Californian Sea Lion occurs all along the west coast of the United States. The male grows to a length of 2.5 m and a weight of over 300 kg; the female is much smaller. Sea Lions are skilful and fast swimmers, hunting for fish and small squids in the sea. In the mating season the males occupy and defend their territories on rocky islands. Each male has approximately thirty mates which he guards so jealously that he does not eat throughout this period. Each female produces a single pup, which she

Californian Sea Lion

Common Seal

usually suckles for 8 months. The young first learn to swim in the shallows, then in the open sea.

COMMON SEAL
Phoca vitulina

The Common Seal is found in northern parts of the Atlantic and Pacific Oceans. The male reaches a length of 2 m and a weight of 150 kg, the female being somewhat smaller. Seals live in small herds, usually in a permanent territory. During the winter they maintain holes in the ice, through which they enter the sea to feed. There they catch fish, crustaceans and molluscs. On a rocky island the female gives birth to a single calf, which is able to swim and dive from birth.

BOTTLE-NOSED DOLPHIN
Tursiops truncatus

The Bottle-nosed Dolphin is widespread in the Atlantic Ocean and the neighbouring seas. It grows to a length of 3 m or more, and lives in large schools. They mainly catch fish and squids. When swimming, they like to jump out of the water, and are very playful. They communicate with each other using various sounds. In late summer the female gives birth to a single calf, which she suckles for a long time and looks after with great care.

NORTH AMERICAN MANATEE
Trichechus manatus

The North American Manatee lives in coastal waters from Florida to eastern Texas

Bottle-nosed Dolphin

North American Manatee

and Mexico. It reaches a length of 4 m and a weight of 1 tonne. These manatees mostly live alone. They swim slowly through the shallows near the seabed, grazing on marine vegetation. An adult consumes up to 45 kg of food per day. Beneath the water, in a sheltered lagoon, the female gives birth to a single young, which she immediately lifts to the surface to take its first breath.

WEST AFRICAN MANATEE
Trichechus senegalensis

The West African Manatee lives in the coastal waters and estuaries of West Africa.

It reaches a length of 4.5 m and a weight of 650 kg. These manatees form small herds. They graze on vegetation near the seabed in shallow water, and on shore plants which dip into the water. Females produce 1 or occasionally 2 young.

DUGONG
Dugong dugon

The Dugong is found in warm regions, in the coastal waters of East Africa, along the coasts of the Red Sea and as far as northern and north-eastern Australia. It reaches

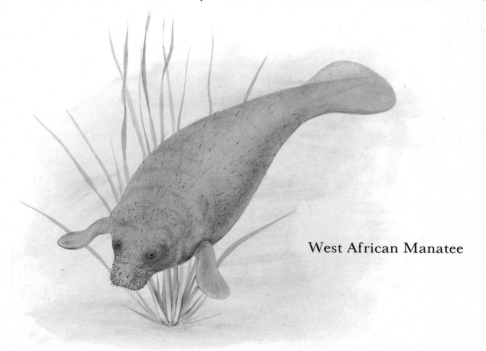
West African Manatee

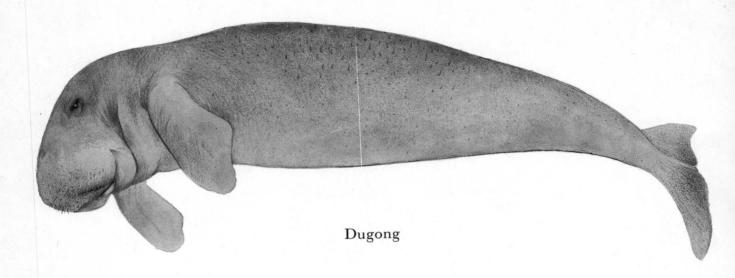

Dugong

a length of 4 m, and an adult weighs 300 — 1 000 kg. Dugongs live solitarily or in pairs, only sometimes forming groups. They feed on various marine plants, grazing during their slow passage along the coast. They occasionally eat crustaceans, particularly crabs, which they catch on the seabed. Females produce 1 or occasionally 2 young.

BIRDS

BLACK-FOOTED PENGUIN
Spheniscus demersus

The Black-footed Penguin is a flightless bird about 65 cm tall which lives on the coast of southern and south-western Africa. It lives in large colonies, individual pairs nesting in fissures in the rocks and between stones, or digging shallow burrows. Both parents incubate the 2 eggs. The young hatch after 38 — 43 days, and both parents feed them. Black-footed Penguins feed mainly on fish, and to a lesser extent on molluscs and small crustaceans.

RED-BILLED TROPICBIRD
Phaethon aethereus

The Red-billed Tropicbird lives in the sea, going ashore to the tropical coastline of South and Central America only during the mating season. This bird, which has a wingspan of 110 cm, is recognizable by its extended tail feathers. It flies high above the surface searching for prey, which it catches by diving vertically into the water. It hunts near the surface, eating small squids, octo-

Black-footed Penguin

Red-billed Tropicbird

puses, fish and crustaceans. In a hollow in the sand or directly on to a rocky overhang the female lays a single egg. Both parents take turns to incubate the egg, and they both feed the young, which can fly only after 70—85 days.

MAGNIFICENT FRIGATEBIRD
Fregata magnificens

The Magnificent Frigatebird lives in tropical coastal districts of Central and South America. It reaches a length of 114 cm, and has a wingspan of 225 cm. It is one of the most skilful of fliers, and spends long hours gliding above the waves in search of prey. It catches fish, molluscs and crustaceans from the surface of the water, in flight, and sometimes steals the prey of terns or skuas. Frigatebirds nest in colonies, building their nests out of branches in a tall bush. Both parents incubate the single egg and feed the young chick, which does not leave the nest for 4—5 months.

Magnificent Frigatebird

Guanay Cormorant

Peruvian Booby

GUANAY CORMORANT
Phalacrocorax bougainvillii

The Guanay Cormorant lives on the rocky islands and cliffs along the coast of Peru. Experts estimate that there are up to 20 million cormorants concentrated in this area. They produce the valuable fertilizer 'guano', because their droppings are rich in phosphates and other mineral substances. The Guanay Cormorant, which is about 65 cm long, feeds mainly on fish. Single pairs make a simple nest, lined with a few feathers, directly on the ground. Both parents take turns to incubate the 3—5 eggs, and both also feed the young on fish.

PERUVIAN BOOBY
Sula variegata

The Peruvian Booby nests in large colonies on the islands around the coast of Peru. It is 65 cm long, with a wingspan of 150 cm. It is an excellent swimmer and diver, hunting its food, mainly fish, molluscs and crustaceans, below the surface. Boobies dive into the water at great speed, after a fast, vertical plummet from the sky. Pairs build their nests of seaweed on cliff ledges. The parent birds take turns to sit on the 1—3 eggs for 42 days, but usually only rear 1 young, which they feed very well.

BROWN PELICAN
Pelecanus occidentalis

The Brown Pelican occurs on the coast and on coastal islands from the southern United States to Peru. It reaches a length of 100 cm and has a wingspan of 225 cm. It catches the fish which form its main food by diving

Brown Pelican

vertically into the water. Brown Pelicans nest in large colonies of up to several hundred pairs, building their nest of sticks and reeds on rocky cliffs or in tall mangroves. Both parents take turns to sit on the eggs for a period of 1 month, then feed the young on fish.

INCA TERN
Larosterna inca

The Inca Tern, about 43 cm long, is found on the islands off the coast of southern Peru and Chile. It nests in large colonies, pairs of these birds usually building their nests, of seaweed or blades of grass, in fissures in the face of steep cliffs. Both parents incubate the 2 eggs, and they feed the young on the nest for 5 weeks. Inca Terns feed on small fish and various marine invertebrates, diving into the water to catch their prey. It is not unusual for them to pursue other terns and steal their prey.

Inca Tern

Common Eider

Common Puffin

COMMON EIDER
Somateria mollissima

The Common Eider lives in the most northerly parts of Europe, Asia and North America. It nests on seashores, surrounding the eggs with a large amount of the down pulled from its breast for which this 60-cm-long duck is famous. The female sits on the 4—5 eggs herself, and as soon as they hatch she takes the ducklings to the water. Eiders feed on molluscs, crustaceans, worms and fish and also on vegetable matter.

COMMON PUFFIN
Fratercula arctica

The Common Puffin, a seabird about 30 cm long, lives in the open sea. During the breeding season large colonies of these birds are found on cliffs and islands, mainly in northern and central parts of the Atlantic. They like to search out grassy banks, in which

they make burrows up to 2 m long. They line the nest chamber with grass, seaweed and feathers, and females usually lay a single egg, which both parents incubate in turn. Both also feed the young. Puffins' diet consists mainly of fish, marine crustaceans and molluscs.

COMMON GUILLEMOT
Uria aalge

The home of the 43-cm-long Common Guillemot is in the Atlantic Ocean. During the breeding season large colonies of these birds are found on coastal rocks, cliffs and islands. On the bare surface of a rocky ledge the female lays a single egg, which both parents take turns to incubate for a total of 35 days. Both also feed the young. Guillemots eat marine crustaceans, molluscs and small fish.

REPTILES

GREEN TURTLE
Chelonia mydas

The Green Turtle is found in the Atlantic, Pacific and Indian Oceans, usually in tropical and subtropical regions. Its shell is up to 1.5 m long, and its total weight is around 250 kg. Green Turtles feed on small marine animals and partly also on seaweed. The female lays up to 200 eggs, which she buries in the sand of tropical shores. The young hatch after 2 months, and make for the sea at once.

LEATHERBACK TURTLE
Dermochelys coriacea

The Leatherback Turtle lives in warm tropical seas. It can grow to a length of 3 m and reach a weight of over 600 kg, and it feeds on animal and vegetable material. In the egg-laying season the female goes ashore on

Common Guillemot

Green Turtle

Leatherback Turtle

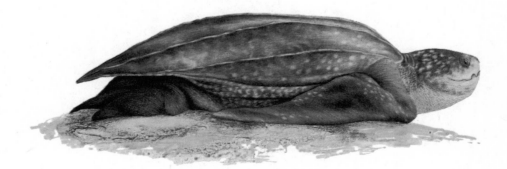

Hawksbill Turtle

a sandy beach, for instance, in Malaya, Mozambique or Jamaica. Each female lays an average of 90 eggs in a hole scraped in the sand, then the young hatch after 2 months and go straight into the sea.

HAWKSBILL TURTLE
Eretmochelys imbricata

The Hawksbill Turtle is found in warm oceans. Its shell is about 90 cm long. These turtles wander the open seas, feeding on small animals and seaweed. The female buries her 100—150 eggs on a sandy beach. The young hatch in 50—60 days, and try to get into the sea as quickly as possible to avoid their predators. The Hawksbill Turtle is one of the most sought-after turtles, on account of its beautiful, high-quality carapace. At present, this species is internation-

Marine Iguana

Yellow-bellied Sea Snake

ally protected in the same way as other marine turtles. Nevertheless, it is still hunted for its tortoiseshell, and local people also eat the meat.

MARINE IGUANA
Amblyrhynchus cristatus

The Marine Iguana lives on the Galápagos Islands; it grows to a length of 120 cm and reaches a weight of 12 kg. It feeds exclusively on seaweed, for which it dives into the sea at low tide. When swimming, it moves with the help of its flat-sided tail. In a hole dug in the ground the female lays 2 eggs, from which the young hatch after 3 months.

YELLOW-LIPPED SEA KRAIT
Laticauda colubrina

The Yellow-lipped Sea Krait is an inhabitant of the tropical seas of the eastern Indian and western Atlantic Oceans. It grows to a length of about 150 cm, and is highly

venomous. It spends its whole life in the sea, coming ashore only to lay its eggs. Immediately after hatching, the young look for the water. Sea Kraits feed on small fish.

YELLOW-BELLIED SEA SNAKE
Pelamis platurus

The Yellow-bellied Sea Snake, which is highly venomous, grows to a length of about

Yellow-lipped Sea Krait

1 m and is found in almost all warm seas. These sea snakes feed on small fish; they spend their whole lives at sea, and the female gives birth to live young in the water. Though their bite is dangerous to humans, these snakes are not aggressive. People fishing who accidentally catch them in their nets can throw them back with their bare hands.

FISH

LESSER SPOTTED DOGFISH
Scyliorhinus caniculus

The Lesser Spotted Dogfish is a small shark found in almost all European seas. It grows to a maximum length of 1 m, and is not dangerous to humans. It hunts molluscs, crustaceans and small fish near the seabed. The female lays up to 20 eggs, which have leathery sheaths and long, thread-like attachments by which they catch onto seaweed and submerged objects. The young hatch after about 9 months.

ATLANTIC MACKEREL
Scomber scombrus

The Atlantic Mackerel is very common in all European seas. It grows to a length of 50 cm and a weight of about 1.5 kg. Mackerel always move around in huge shoals, and are found inshore in summer, in winter at greater depths. Spawning takes place from May to August; a single female can produce 400 000 — 500 000 eggs. Young Mackerel feed on small crustaceans, while adult fish follow shoals of herring, sprats and other smaller fish.

ANGLERFISH
Lophius piscatorius

Along the coast of western Europe and the northern part of the Mediterranean lives the strange Anglerfish. It reaches a length of up to 2 m. These fish stay close to the seabed, usually burying themselves in the mud, where they are perfectly camouflaged. With their long spines, looking like marine worms, they bait other fish, which they then

Lesser Spotted Dogfish

Atlantic Mackerel

Anglerfish

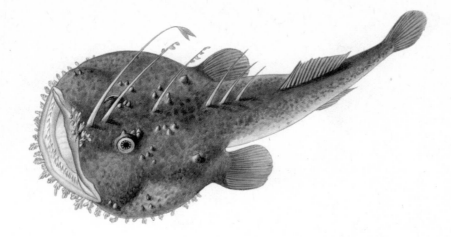

easily overcome. Anglerfish spawn at a depth of up to 2 000 m. The eggs are shed in ribbons which rise to the surface, where the fry hatch from them.

INVERTEBRATES

COMMON EUROPEAN OYSTER
Ostrea edulis

The Common European Oyster is among the best-known of marine bivalve molluscs. They grow to a diameter of 8—10 cm, and reproduce after only a year. They live in huge colonies. Adult oysters attach themselves to a firm surface and filter plankton from the water. They are often grown in specially protected farms in shallow waters, and at the age of 3 years are removed to be sold as food. They are eaten raw.

COMMON GOOSE BARNACLE
Lepas anatifera

The Common Goose Barnacle, which is widespread along sea coasts, is a small crustacean which lives in a special shell, attached by a stalk to an underwater rock or other surface. Six pairs of whip-like legs protrude

Common European Oyster

Common Goose Barnacle

395

Hermit Crab

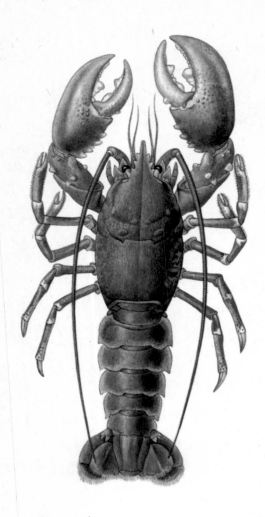

Common Lobster

COMMON LOBSTER
Homarus gammarus

The home of the Common Lobster is among the underwater rocks along the coast of the Atlantic. This crustacean is some 50 cm long with its large claws. It feeds on molluscs, echinoderms, fish and other marine animals, which it hunts at night. Every other year the female produces many thousands of eggs, which she carries attached beneath her body for 11 months, until the larvae hatch. Lobster meat is considered a great delicacy.

HERMIT CRAB
Eupagurus bernhardus

The Hermit Crab, which grows to a length of about 3.5 cm, is common along European coasts. It has a soft, vulnerable belly, and protects itself inside empty mollusc shells. It feeds on small animals and organic remains, which it collects on the seabed.

from the shell, which the barnacle uses to stir the water and move food towards itself. It lives on tiny animals and algae.

INDEX OF COMMON NAMES

Page numbers in italics refer to illustrations

INDEX OF LATIN NAMES